D0458085

MOLLY RADFORD, M.D.

MOLLY RADFORD, M.D.

By

MOLLY RADFORD WARD

author of

Bill Martin, American

VANTAGE PRESS

New York   Washington   Hollywood

CONTENTS

MOLLY RADFORD, M.D.

CHAPTER I. IDYLLIC CHILDHOOD

The Island

(MARY)

As usual, I was looking for Molly. Even at age five she had a habit of suddenly not being where I thought she was. We were on the Island as it was summertime, but much as she loved the water I was confident that she was neither in nor on it—that was one rule that the Steve Radford family had which was never violated. No one, young or old, swam or boated alone. I had looked high and low about the two cottages we used for summer living but was not ready to search the entire eleven acres as yet. It was still midafternoon and I felt sure she would turn up when it suited her even though she frequently would not answer my calling to her unless my voice sounded really angry.

As I approached the main cottage I just happened to look high enough! There was my ragged, dirty tomboy perched on a limb of a big oak tree which stood about twenty or thirty feet from the front porch. The limb was a good twelve feet above the ground. Her back was against the large trunk of the tree, her legs straddling the limb, and she appeared to be as comfortable as if she were in a rocking chair.

"Molly, what are you doing up there? How did you get up there and how are you going to get down?"

The nonchalant child looked down at me and said, "Oh, I always come up here when I want to be alone."

Whereupon she crawled a couple of feet to the rope of the long swing and slid down it to a sitting position on the board seat of the swing. Poking her bare toes in the soft dirt she peacefully began to sway back and forth. Abruptly she stopped, stood up, casually stepped to the great tree trunk, and with little fingers and prehensile toes swarmed up the rough bark to "her limb." Standing up on it she said to me, "See, it's easy. Before Papa put up the swing sometimes I came up here but it wasn't so easy to get down. Since he put those knots on one side of the rope I can come up that way. Now I'm learning to climb the smooth side hand-over-hand."

What was there to say to such a monkey? As I started to turn toward the house Molly slid halfway down the rope, put her legs through the two rings attached there, and hung by her knees with her fine blond hair blowing about her grinning, dirty face. Her brown eyes regarding me upside down seemed to ask me to understand why she needed her own place for her private thoughts and dreams. She never did tell me or anyone else what these were and I doubt that she remembered them herself years later.

Phyllis, her sister, who was four years older, was calmly sitting reading on the front porch, and hadn't even looked up at this interchange. How could it be that I had produced such totally different little beings? It was about time to go over to the second cottage which was used for cooking, eating, storage, etc. Preparing a meal in those days with few conveniences of any kind took some hours. Steve was bringing a couple of friends with their two children for supper and overnight. They would drive out from Oshkosh, Wisconsin, our home, fourteen miles south along the shore of Lake Winnebago.

I called both girls to come with me and we three were soon shelling a large batch of fresh green peas on the little front stoop of the dining cottage. The tenant farmer who lived on the mainland about a thousand feet across from the Island had brought them along with a couple of freshly killed and dressed chickens and some eggs.

He, Nordhause, and his family took care of the quite large garden and farm animals in return for their living. However, Steve had started raising collies on the Island, planning to develop a new breed of all-white collies. The "hired man" fed these and milked the two Jersey cows who, for some reason, were also kept on the Island instead of at the farm.

2

When the peas were shelled, Molly suddenly disappeared again but I didn't give it a thought for it wasn't hard to guess that this time she would be with Nordhause in a large, ramshackle building. This had formerly been the dining and kitchen hall for the families who had spent summers there in a communal sort of living arrangement some years before Steve bought the Island. There Molly would be watching the "hired man" preparing the large tubs of dog food consisting of old dried bread and "soup" made from bones and cast-off entrails, etc., collected from neighboring farms.

After the dogs were fed, I knew that Molly and the man would be at the farther side of the Island in the rather tumbled-down structure which served as a cow shed. The man would be milking and Molly, while watching him intently, would be hanging on to a cow's tail to keep it from switching into the milker's face. This would be repeated early in the morning when almost everyone else was still asleep.

As I was finishing the ice cream mixture made from last evening's cream which had risen in the large flat pans set out each day, I heard a horn blow. Across the channel Steve's horse and buggy and the guests' carriage had arrived. There was a rowboat on that side but the one Nordhause had brought over was needed since there were four extra people and their luggage. At the sound of the horn Molly came rushing up to me, yelling,

"Can't I go over with Nordy to get them? Please," she added, "I haven't been out all day!"

"Out" to her, the little water baby, meant, of course, on the lake. I regretfully said no, as there wouldn't be room. However, I did promise her the pleasure of a late afternoon swim as I was certain that Steve and guests would welcome a dip after their dusty drive. Then she saw what I was doing, making ice cream. Although that wasn't an unusual dessert for a family which had two Jersey cows, it was chocolate, Molly's favorite.

"Can I lick the dasher?"

"Of course you may but Phyllis and your two guests will share it with you—that is, any or all of you four who take turns cranking the freezer."

3

Satisfied, Molly ran down to the dock to await the row-boats. Phyllis, being nine, was expected to help me fix the oatmeal over the kerosine stove before it went into the fire-less cooker. She was always a willing helper. She liked food and, like me, was always ready for a chat about all sorts of things—this time it was about the book she had been read-ing.

She was a most proper little girl who was getting more in-terested in clothes and soon left for the other house to put on a new dress for the company. I never worried about that too much because she spent plenty of time swimming, canoeing, and romping with the dogs out in the fresh air.

Molly was soon in her bathing suit as were Steve and the guests' children. We all went down to watch the swimmers who had a gay time splashing about. Molly and Steve seemed to be having a private conference on the way up to the house but it obviously appeared to be secret so I asked no questions. It being a Saturday, all of us would have a re-laxing day ahead of us, so we sat up a bit later than usual chatting and watching the stars and moon over the water. I was interested in all the news of town which Alice, our next door neighbor, could tell me as I hadn't been in town for two or three weeks. Bert and Steve discussed business. They were both in lumber companies, Bert with the Paine Lumber Co., the largest in Oshkosh, and Steve was with the Radford Sash and Door Company which his father had founded a good many years before.

The children were sent up to bed at a reasonable hour to sleep on mattresses on the front and back screened porches on the second floor. We were sure that they were not sleep-ing but were probably looking at the big moon. Phyllis and Chandler, the same age, were probably talking seriously about something, and Bob, Molly's age, was probably draw-ing pictures in the moonlight on the wall and cracking jokes—we could hear their giggling down below. However, we knew they would be sleeping soon—after the swim and all the fresh air.

In the middle of the night a sudden storm blew up, as sometimes happens on that thirty-mile-long lake. Thunder, lightning, and howling wind woke us up. Steve and I dashed

4

up the stairs from our first-floor bedroom to find the relatively unperturbed four children dragging the mattresses in from the east porch where the rain was driving through the screens. Alice and Bert, in dressing gowns and looking rather upset, were standing in their bedroom doorway watching the youngsters spread the bedding on the floor of the roomy upstairs hall. I checked the blankets and found none had gotten wet. The self-reliant kids had dragged everything in at the first warning thunder and lightning.

Steve and I had pretty well instilled in our children a feeling of what to fear and what should be taken as natural phenomena: when outside in a storm never to stand under a tree; never to go in or stay in the water, etc. As infants they had instinctively cried at loud claps of thunder, but by this time they rather enjoyed the drama of a real electrical storm. Though severe, this one subsided in less than an hour and all was peaceful and everyone asleep soon after it had passed over the Island.

The next morning the children were missing. Alice came downstairs in some alarm but I told her what I presumed had happened. Molly, since she was three or four, always arose about dawn to race over "her Island," usually to meet Nordhause at or near the cow shed to supervise the milking. This morning Steve and I were quite sure that she had aroused the others to go with her to inspect the storm damage and to rescue small birds which often were to be found injured among the torn-off branches and/or uprooted trees which littered the ground after every severe storm.

Before long the four of them appeared triumphantly, each carrying one or two "orphans of the storm." Phyllis and Molly showed the boys where to find boxes and rags to put the poor little things in. Bread crumbs and water were supplied and the children tenderly watched over their patients a good part of the morning after they themselves had consumed a hearty breakfast.

Since the sun came out full blast there was no reason to cancel the picnic luncheon I had planned for the noon meal. All we had to do was to spread a few blankets on the wet ground and makeshift wooden seats near the dock. Naturally a swim was in order before the repast. Alice, Bert, and I did not care to take part in that but Steve and the children started into the shallow water. Oddly enough, Molly, although she was in her bathing suit, hung back from the rest.

I began to wonder if she was not feeling well after all the excitement. However, before I could reach her she scampered along the dock at water level, raced up the steps to the higher part of the dock where visitors' boats could tie up. It was about five feet above the water surface at that point where the depth was over an adult's head. Two of the dogs had followed her. My small daughter walked to the edge of the dock, took one look at her father who was in the water but some distance away, and then dove headfirst!

Alice and I gasped. Bert was on his feet. Phyllis, Chandler, and Bob stopped splashing in the shallower water. Steve calmly swam about in a circle as Molly's little wet head rose to the surface. In the few seconds between Molly's dive and her reappearance, Tip, one of her very favorite collies, had leapt off the "high" dock and was swimming frantically toward her. Molly was calmly "dog-paddling" toward her father and shore when Tip caught up with her and grabbed her suit in his teeth. The child, almost angrily, tried to beat him off. Soon she reached a depth where she could stand with her head above water and Tip splashed to the low part of the dock and scrambled out.

All the swimmers came ashore. Molly was understandably proud of her first "high dive" in front of witnesses but she was a bit more than abashed that she had to share deserved praise with Tip! (None of our collies ever liked water and would never venture into it except to drink and get their feet wet in hot weather.) Molly was too young to appreciate the dog's devotion and courage and must have felt that her accomplishment had been rudely spoiled by her favorite friend. However, she and Steve chortled over the success of their great surprise which they had been planning for about a week!

The day ended pleasantly with the Osborns taking off in the rowboat to the mainland and their late afternoon drive back to town. While I was preparing the small snack supper I had many things to think about. With good reason, I had always feared the lake, although I believe I was successful in keeping that fear from my children. My thoughts turned back to twenty-four years before.

It was on a similar warm August day in 1886 when my mother, father, two younger sisters, Hattie and Kittleen, and assorted aunts, uncles, and cousins had had a picnic by this same lake shore in Oshkosh. Before eating, the children had begged my father to take them for a ride in a rowboat. Father, Edward Hughes, agreed, and Hattie, aged seven, Cousin Willy Bray about the same age, and little Kittleen crawled into the boat. Father shoved it off the sand beach and they started off on the calm water. For some reason I, at age eleven, did not want to go. As I remember, it was chiefly because I loved being with my mother, who worked all week-days with father in his department store. It had not been too long before that my third sister, Sarah (Sasie), had died of scarlet fever. I was old enough to feel my mother's great grief and wanted to be near her whenever possible.

Shouts came from the lake. We could see a boat had turned over and a second boat was being rowed frantically toward it. We on shore couldn't see at that distance which boat was which. After what seemed like an eternity one boat came to the shore. In it were two comparative strangers with a drenched and hysterical Hattie and a half-drowned, spluttering Willy Bray—no one else. We pieced out the terrible story from Hattie's frantic, sob-ridden account.

Kitty, in the bow, had become seasick and frightened, tried to get to my father at the oars, stumbled over athwart, and fell over the side. Father reached out frantically to catch her, and the boat overturned. Father grabbed a dress and shoved Hattie up onto the bottom of the over-turned boat. In seconds he had hold of a small arm and while hanging on to the boat's gunwale, tried to hand Kitty up to her sister. Little wet hands slipped and the four-year-old disappeared. Father let go of the boat and went after her. Neither was seen again. The rescue boat drew near and had picked up Willy on the other side of father's boat. Willy had, miraculously, managed to tread water—he had swallowed and inhaled a good deal but was alive. The rescue men took the terrified Hattie off her perch and spent a bit of time looking for the others. There was no sign of anything except two floating oars and bits of debris. Like many people who lived on the shores of Lake Winnebago in those days, my father and the two rescuers had never learned to swim!

The pathetic bodies were washed ashore two days later.

That was all a long time ago, but that day and the aftermath of the effect on my dear mother as well as on my young sister, who had nightmares for weeks to follow, were still fresh in my memory.

Since I had much to do, feeding my family, washing the dishes at the primative sink with its pump for fresh water (all hot water had to be heated on the stove), I ceased to reminisce. Getting ready for the next day's meals, hunting up Molly to send her off to bed, and putting the house in order filled my thoughts. However, when Steve and I were in bed and he went promptly to sleep, the past came back with a rush, keeping me awake for some hours.

A very few years after Steve and I were married he bought the Island from the corporation which had owned it. Most of the buildings on it were still standing but in a bad state of repair. He knew of my fear of the lake but dismissed it quite casually, saying he'd teach me to swim. We were to spend our summers out there and that was that. He was the boss and I loved him. When John, our first child, was about a year old, we moved to the Island and Steve taught me to swim. Each summer thereafter became easier for me to take although there was much hard work. I did have some occasional help from daughters of immigrant farmers, and the days were lovely. I taught each of the "hired girls" to swim as well as little John when he was about three years old. He adored going out in the old Wooden Shoe, a high-sided safe tub of a sailboat which I even began to enjoy myself when the lake was not too rough.

Then John became very ill and we moved back to town in late July of 1902. The terrible days that followed—John had meningitis and the specialist who came from Chicago said he couldn't live more than three weeks—somehow didn't bring Steve and me closer. We each suffered our agonizing grief separately and alone, when John died August 19, 1902, at age four and a half.

8

Phyllis about 1½ years old, a delightful, healthy baby, was my only consolation. It was about then that I started to read omnivorously but especially in philosophy and religion. Although I never went to college as Harriet and our cousin Katie had done—even two of my father's sisters had done so, too—I'd had a good background of schooling in Chicago after my mother died. My Aunt Harriet and her Danish husband had taken me in to live with them. Aunt Margaret Bray, Willy's mother, had taken Hattie. These blessed aunts had even given me a wonderful six months in Europe.

My reading, my devoted aunts, and my new child somehow got me through the next few years. Some of the acute pain and grief lessened when Molly was on the way. Steve, even, seemed to come out of his shell and immediately planned on having a son.

Bert Clark, our friend and fine young family doctor, arrived at our house on Algoma Street on Ground Hog Day just in time to welcome Molly into the world. She came with a rush as the "bag of waters" broke and Bert was drenched!

"Damn it, Mary, that kid of yours ought to grow up to be a swimmer!"

Both Steve and I had a good laugh. Bert borrowed some of Steve's clothes before he went out into the cold February snow and wind. I had a good temporary nurse to look after Phyllis who was almost four, the new baby and me, and I was content. Steve seemed pleased that all had gone well and was more attentive to me than he had been for some time. However, I knew he was sadly disappointed that the baby was not a boy. We seriously considered naming her Stephanie!

Now, in my late night recollections, I was happy that Steve decided to name her Mary, after me, but to always call her Molly. I was convinced that my five-year-old tomboy would have disliked Stephanie, and even my husband would not have wanted to call her Steve!

I finally went to sleep knowing that we both loved her as much as we did Phyllis in spite of her being unpredictable and even exasperating at times.

DOGS

The next few years passed happily enough. Summers at the Island were peaceful and wonderful for both girls. Steve's collie kennels were thriving and he did a fine job in selective breeding; producing, eventually, handsome all-white Scotch collies. He soon followed up on a very good idea he had. He sold a good many of the farmers in Winnebago county on the idea of taking a pregnant female as their own farm dog. Most of the families had dairy farms and collies are noted for being excellent herding dogs. As it turned out in most cases, the "farmed out" bitches turned out right from the start and herded not only cows but pigs and even chickens. Then when the pups were born they had more individual care, were weaned and partly trained by the farm women and children, and gave pleasure to all. Steve paid for the pups by weight when they were to be sold.

During the summers Molly usually went with her father in the old buggy to make the rounds of these farms. Before this new system was started the expectant mother dogs frequently escaped from their poorly built pens (Nordhause was getting old and sloppy in his work), and would have their pups under one or another tumbled-down cottage. At such times Molly and the old man would go from one old house to another listening for the squalling of puppies under the dilapidated flooring. When the nests were spotted, Molly, being very skinny, would crawl on elbows and stomach under the building and return to the waiting man with a tiny, squirming pup in each dirty hand. She would make each trip with the anxious but trusting mother crawling beside her until all five to eight progeny were retrieved. This was wonderful for Molly but somewhat of a nuisance and worry to the rest of us. Also, the number of dogs grew to such an extent that they couldn't be properly cared for or housed.

I often wondered how Steve could spend so much time away from his lumber business to take those frequent jaunts about the countryside. However, he was getting fine healthy puppies and was selling them pretty well over the country. Although he was normally not a very patient man he had done a remarkable job during the selective breeding process. I never questioned him about how, where, and what he was doing. He seemed happy and aside from Molly's cut feet when she stepped on dog bones, her occasional barbed-wire cuts, broken bones, and skinned knees the girls had happy summers.

The normal amount of primative housework and meal preparations kept me occupied. I really loved the Island life, the beautiful dogs, and the peace. My old fears gradually disappeared except when the girls were out in the canoe Steve bought—he even had a sail made for it. However, although they both were allowed to paddle it about in the harbor alone, Steve always went with them when they sailed the fragile, "tippy" craft with no keel and no sideboards. I enjoyed fishing for the bass, pickerel, and pike from the dock or trolling from the back of the rowboat.

Both girls became excellent swimmers and when Phyllis was twelve she swam from the dock to Nevitt's Point a mile away, with the rest of us keeping close-by in the boat. Molly at eight insisted on trying the same the following day. Much to her disgust the lake became very choppy and halfway over she had to give up. Nevertheless she swam her mile back and forth in the protected harbor.

One collie was named Nordica. For some unexplained reason she was completely a "people dog" and disliked and feared the rest of her kind. The other dogs sensed this fear and unmercifully "ganged up" on her. Her only recourse was to take to the water which, like most collies, she feared and hated. Of necessity she became a good swimmer and spent many hours each day following the rowboat whenever it went back and forth across the channel. Steve called her a coward and I believe the only reason he kept her was that she had fine pups (who didn't inherit her ideosyncracies). I admired and loved her more than any of the others. After all, hadn't she shown exceptional courage in conquering her instinctive fear of water? She and I had much in common, and in spite of Steve's contempt for her she was my dog and my friend who spent most of her non-swimming hours with me.

One episode I must relate before we "go to town." One

11

morning when Phyllis was about twelve and Molly eight, Nordhause, the hired man, didn't show up. Steve had not yet left and the two cows were bellowing to be milked. What to do? I had refused to learn to milk, and Steve, surprisingly enough, admitted that he couldn't either. Up until then I had supposed that he was able to do anything. We were in a quandary and Steve was about to row over to the mainland to try to find someone on a nearby farm who would help him out. Phyllis and Molly spoke up together.

"We can milk Bessie and Polly."

Steve and I looked at each other. He said, "I don't believe it."

I replied, "Well, you might as well let them try."

An hour or so later both girls returned with full buckets which they had to carry between them, one at a time.

The Radford family stopped going to the Island for the summers when Phyllis went to Vassar in 1918. The dogs were moved from there ultimately to a farm west of Oshkosh. Some fifty-odd years later Molly received a letter from one Mary McMillan, a collie lover, who asked a number of questions about the White Collies who went to the Coolidges in the White House. Miss McMillan stated that a number of dog magazines had written up stories of White House dogs and that some TV programs had recently put on some shows concerning the same subject. She added that she was sure some of the White Collie stories were inaccurate. By writing to a Radford relative in Oshkosh, her letter finally reached Molly in Santa Fe, New Mexico.

The result was that Molly wrote up from memory the story of Rob Roy and Prudence Prim which Mary McMillan submitted to COLLIE CUES. It was printed in the August 1971 issue of that magazine. The following is a copy of that article.

ROB ROY—WHITE COLLIE IN THE WHITE HOUSE
By Molly Radford Ward
(Submitted by M. McMillan, Fox River Grove, Illinois)

After over fifty years, I have recently been informed by Mary McMillan, of Fox River Grove, Illinois, that White House dogs have been written up for several publications as well as TV programs. I have read one or two of these articles which contain many inaccuracies as far as the White Collies of President and Mrs. Coolidge are concerned.

My Father, Stephen Radford, developed the first all-white collies in the United States, by long and patient selective breeding in the early 1900s. One great and puzzling problem was the appearance of deafness in some of the all-white pups. This, of course, had to be bred out of the new strains.

By about 1915 he had a good number of magnificent white collies. Because they (and we for the summers) lived on an island in Lake Winnebago outside of Oshkosh, Wisconsin, the kennels were called ISLAND WHITE SCOTCH COLLIE KENNELS.

Some of the dogs were shown in those days and won a fair number of blue ribbons. Because of the lack of knowledge then about immunization against various diseases, some of the dogs returned to the kennels with infections which they passed on to others, and my father, Steve, wisely discontinued showing any of them.

Rob Roy was the star of the kennel both in looks and intelligence. His registered name was SIR PRIZE. (To my sister and me, when we were teenagers, he was Tige.) When he was about four years old, father got an order from Ringling Brothers Circus for a white collie to be used in a spectacular act. (Previous to this time, I believe, poodles were used mostly as performing dogs.)

Father, believing rightly, I think, that it would be good advertizing, shipped SIR PRIZE to the circus's winter headquarters at Sarasota, Florida. In transit, somewhere in Ohio, the dog's crate fell off an old horse-drawn express wagon, broke, and "Tige" escaped. What followed was a "Lassie Come Home" tale.

Approximately two and a half months later our "Tige," not looking much like the vaunted SIR PRIZE, arrived in Oshkosh. Friends of father's recognized beneath the dirt and matted coat the thoroughbred collie that it was and brought him to the kennels. He was carefully nursed back to health and good condition, and sired one more batch of pups about the time that President Harding died.

Father then had the bright idea of sending him to the White House as a gift to the Coolidges. Shortly thereafter lovely Mrs. Coolidge wrote father a letter telling us that he had been rechristened Rob Roy, that he had adapted himself to the ways of the President and was always at his bedroom or office door at the exact moment when Mr. Coolidge was ready to open it. He was more or less a constant companion of the President until he died.

I don't know when Howard Chandler Christy painted the picture of Rob Roy and Mrs. Coolidge in one of the White House gardens, but I saw it hanging in the tourist part of the White House in 1932. The story about dyeing the dog red instead of having Mrs. Coolidge wear a red gown is probably apocryphal, but it could be true. What I do know, lovely as the painting is, Christy did not do justice to Rob Roy in that he gave the dog the rather long narrow nose and head of the later more popular fashion for collies. Rob Roy and his descendants (whom I knew) had the broader brow and shorter nose of the original Scotch collies, which all of our dogs had while my father had anything to do with their raising and breeding.

Prudence Prim was also a gift from my father to the Coolidges. I think she was sent about a year after Rob Roy as a mate or companion for him. This I know, except for exact dates, and I know of no puppies born to them. She, we heard, died within about a year of going to the White House and, I think, Rob Roy was killed by a car sometime thereafter.

Addendum: Some relatively short time after Rob Roy went to the White House, father got an order from Point Barrow, Alaska, for several white collies to help herd the U.S.-owned reindeer up there. Because they were white, intelligent, and good herding dogs without being fierce enough, as were the huskies they'd been using, they would not kill the deer.

Some of Rob Roy's descendants were in that group

which did such a fine job up there that my mother received two gorgeous white fox pelts as a thank-you. My sister wore the luxurious fur stole made from these, but they were stolen from her hotel room in Texas, when she was on a business trip a few years later.

TOWN

Naturally, childhood does not consist of just summers. However, I am happy to recall that the nine or ten months in "town" were pretty ideal for my girls, certainly compared with the youthful experience of almost any person forty or fifty years later.

Typically, Molly balked at leaving "her Island" every year when it was time to return to town.

"I'll have to wear shoes! I'll have to wear dresses and even take baths often instead of swimming!"

Often she would be missing when it was time to cross the channel for the trip into town with our various belongings. When this happened on one occasion I was calling and searching for her, so was not at the dock to more or less supervise the loading of the rowboats which had to make several trips to the large car which Steve had rented. In earlier years we had chartered a fair-sized launch to take us directly from Oshkosh to the Island and back—but money seemed to be getting scarcer.

In any case, with Molly firmly held by the hand, I arrived at the dock in time to see one of the men who came to help who was loading my large foot-pedal sewing machine. He was placing it on top of a pile of things which had already overloaded the rowboat.

"Please don't put that on this load, the boat is already too full."

"But, ma'am, Mr. Radford ordered me to take this and all the rest on this trip, to save time," said the tired man.

All I could say was to wait a few minutes. Then I went to find Steve who was giving last instructions to the "hired man" about the dogs, etc.

Steve said in response to my query, "The boat is not overloaded—it is perfectly safe."

Molly and I walked back to the dock where Phyllis, all properly dressed for town, was quietly reading. We sat down on a bench while man and boat started off. About halfway over to the mainland the big sewing machine apparently shifted slightly and the boat went over. A chill ran through me as I remembered another boat. This time I knew that the nice young man in it could swim very well. Steve appeared at the dock in time to see the swimmer trying to gather up the assorted articles which floated. Fortunately the other boat was on its return trip and saved young Paul from a five-hundred-foot swim back to the Island.

I had grown up enough by that time to know not to say, "I told you so!" Steve was silent. The young men landed. They had managed to right the empty, overturned boat and had towed it back.

Paul, dripping wet, but otherwise all right, said to me, "You were right, ma'am. I'm sorry we lost your machine and the other things."

Steve looked at the young men and then at me. There was a question in his eyes, but he said nothing.

I answered his wordless question by saying, "It doesn't matter as long as no lives were lost and no one hurt."

I turned, and with Molly in tow, went back to the house to search for possibly last-minute forgotten things and to make Molly wash her face and hands. I believe that was the first time either of the girls had witnessed a real impasse between their parents. Molly, I know, never forgot the incident.

Back in town each fall the girls returned to school. Phyllis and Chandler both were good students. Being the same age and in the same class they enjoyed competing with each other in their studies. (They later graduated as valedictorian and salutatorian of their high school class, about two points apart in their respective total grades.)

The four children walked to school, two by two from kindergarten on. I was grateful that we had a fine normal school (much later a teacher's college) available to them.

When Robert Osborn (who considerably later became the very well known artist and cartoonist) and Molly were in about the seventh or eighth grade, Miss Marvin, their room teacher, asked Bob one day, "Why is it that you and Molly don't do as good work as Phyllis and Chandler did when they were your age—certainly you both have as good minds as your brother and her sister?"

"I don't know, Miss Marvin, but we have so much fun doing other things beside studying."

That, which Miss Marvin reported to Mrs. Osborn and me later, was probably the truest thing ever said!

(According to the customs of the day, Alice Osborn and I always called each other Mrs. Radford and Mrs. Osborn; we started using first names about twenty years later.)

Bob had a wonderful sense of humor and was a good foil for my relatively solemn little girl. What they talked about during their many hours together no one ever knew. However, they thought so much alike in their early days that they held to their firm belief in Santa Claus long after most children were disabused of that wonderful faith.

Time seldom hung heavy on their hands. Walking back and forth to school, during weekends or vacations, they spent most of their waking hours thinking up things to do. In winter our back yard, which was never kept in presentable shape, was always flooded and made a fine skating rink for all. Molly and Phyllis learned to skate when they were so young their skates were of wood and had double runners. Steve, who was a nature lover and almost a fanatic when it came to sports and exercise, saw to it that the girls had everything in the way of sleds, hockey sticks, toboggans, and snow shoes. There being no hills, they didn't learn to ski as children but later on when he bought Molly a horse she and Bob used to skijor behind him.

For the most part Molly and Bob devised their own exercise and amusement. When the snow was deep the two of them did their share of shoveling it off the rink. However, they saw to it that most of it was piled on the north side against the Osborn's barn. This provided a lovely safe landing spot for them when they indulged in sliding off the barn roof. They built many a snow man but most winters concentrated on making snow houses big enough for the two of them to get into and pretend they were Eskimos.

In bad weather they retired to the Osborn clean, warm basement. There, Bob and Chan had a foot-pedaled jig-saw.

With both fathers in the lumber business there was no lack of scrap wood. Bob and Molly happily made birdhouses and numerous other things. Their most successful productions were jig-saw puzzles. Bob, with his great talent for drawing, often sketched out a design on a suitable piece of plywood and they would both take turns in cutting out fantastically shaped small pieces to later confound anyone who tried to put the puzzles together. Often they would paste a picture from a magazine onto the board—resulting in a more colorful puzzle gift.

In spring when it was a bit warmer they played in the sweet-smelling hay on the floor above the Osborn horses and carriages. This made wonderful sliding—especially exciting when they at last dared to go right on through the chute which led to the horses' mangers. As it got warmer and all snow was gone they ventured out on to the many-gabled roof of the barn. This was unbeknownst to me, Steve, or the Osborns.

I only discovered it one day when, looking for Molly as usual, I looked higher than ever before. To my great consternation I saw, there on the highest ridge pole, two small figures—well over two stories above the ground. I shouted to them,

"Robert, Molly, come down from there this minute!"

With a casual wave of the hand each started crawling along that precipitous ridge and then disappeared. They presumably slid down the gutter to the next roof at right angles to the other, which covered the stable and cow barn. I had frantically run around to the back in time to see them crawling down the last slope till they reached a large box from which they could jump to the ground.

They stood in front of me, both very dirty and with several tears in their clothing. They appeared quite nonchalant but not exactly gleeful.

"What on earth made you do such a thing? You must know that it is very dangerous and you could have gotten badly hurt."

"We wanted to see what the town looked like from there," said Molly. "We could see all over, even to the river and the lake!"

Robert, who was rather plump in those days, said, "Molly had to push me up the steep gutters." He wasn't putting all the blame for the escapade on my Molly, but I suspect that he might have been implying that *he* would not have achieved such a height if Molly hadn't given him the extra shoves.

I reported the whole thing to Mrs. Osborn and to Steve. All we could hope for was that our worry and anger would sink in and prevent a repetition. At least we never saw them go that high again. To me a certain satisfaction (maybe revenge?) came when bath time gave me a chance to remove many splinters from my nine-year-old's hands and bottom. Molly didn't often cry except when severely hurt. However, she could yell the house down when a needle approached to remove a splinter. She did the same when anything else she didn't like was about to happen. Funny child; when the needle stuck or the other something happened, there was no further sound—perhaps just a few tears. Many a time did I hear that the Hicks family on the other side of our house, and whom we didn't know very well, fully believed that I spanked Molly at least twice a day. I now admit that I did spank her—even with a hairbrush on drastic occasions—but never that often! Quite a few shrieks emitted from the Radford home that day due to the sight of the needle—not the hurt child.

It was beyond Steve and me to understand why Phyllis never needed nor received a spanking. She was always neat, clean, polite, studious but still a normal, happy, healthy child. Partly because of their appearance and partly due to the fact that I was usually laughing at Molly's numerous activities, friends, sometimes fairly close friends, thought that Phyllis was by far my favorite. This was distinctly not true. When I mentioned that to Molly many years later she pleased and surprised me by saying.

"I really never thought about it. Phyl's interests, likes, and dislikes, were so different from mine it never occurred to me to envy her in any way. In fact I'm quite sure that I always assumed that you loved me as much if not more than you did her."

What Molly expressed so very many years later to me had

always been true. Because that was so, I had been wiser than I knew when I ignored such remarks about favoritism. Also, although the enormous difference in their makeups puzzled me, I was grateful that they seldom quarreled with each other as so many siblings are wont to do.

Chandler and Robert fought fiercely during their early youth but often their struggles came to nothing. Robert's priceless sense of humor usually sent Chandler into stitches of laughter and the younger, plump little boy escaped to safety. In each case, Mrs. Osborn and I used to wonder if our offspring would grow up to be friends—that is, the two girls and the two boys.

For myself, I remembered clearly how my mother, who died of cancer when I was sixteen and Harriet was twelve, would pray that her two girls would grow up to be friends, despite their differences. We did, eventually, become very close, due principally to Hattie's generosity during my most difficult marital and financial troubles.

Phyllis played "lady doll" with her great friend Kathryn Sawyer across the street, was an excellent student, took interest in her clothes, practiced her piano lessons faithfully, and had and enjoyed very pretty dressed-up birthday parties with her friends.

Molly was usually being dragged out from under a pile of scrambled neighbor boys by the Osborn's cook who would say to me, "Mrs. Radford, those bigger boys will be the death of your poor little girl yet!"

Molly would only reply by pulling herself away to run back to the football or baseball game which was still in progress. She was proud that the boys would let her play with them.

Much of the time Bob and Molly continued to be busy in their own pursuits. Real spring brought the interest of tapping the maple trees in their respective yards. No one, to my knowledge, had ever told them about this procedure. Oshkosh was certainly not a maple syrup or sugar area. Molly and Bob scrounged a few nails, pieces of wire, some jelly glasses, and set to work. They carefully selected good-sized straws from the Osborn stable and inserted these into fairly deep holes in the tree trunks at the proper angle. The jelly glasses were hung under the straws and the sap began to drip.

The first day of the first year of this new project, Mrs. Osborn and I happened to call to the kids at the same time to come in for supper. The young voices, in unison, replied, "We can't, we're too busy."

"What are you so busy about?" we called.

"We've got to watch the sap run."

Steve arrived home about that time and said, "Oh, leave them alone. They'll come in when they are really hungry."

This went on for a number of days. A holiday from school gave them many daylight hours. Many meals were delayed and many holes were poked in the trees. The upshot was that the small jelly glasses filled and were dumped into a five-gallon container, scrounged from somewhere. When the large pail was full the two carried it first to the Radford kitchen. The temporary "hired girl" said, "No, not on my stove—that'll take days to boil down." The two got the same response from the Osborn cook.

Nothing daunted, the two twelve-year-olds went to the sandbox in the Osborn's back yard between the clothes line and the Osborn's lovely garden. They were too grown up for sand castles by then and didn't hesitate to break it apart and to construct a very respectable fire pit over which they erected a metal pole for suspending a large dutch oven which Bert Osborn used on duck-hunting trips in the fall. The sap was poured in after the boy and girl had built a good-sized fire under the kettle.

Fortunately there was no rain and Bob and Molly spent their daylight hours begging, borrowing, stealing, and chopping wood to keep the fire burning. Each night they would bank the coals with ashes and resume in the mornings. They never asked for any help, got plenty of exercise and fresh air. We adults admired their perseverance and did not interfere.

The great day came when the five gallons of sap was reduced to about a large glassful of real syrup. No one dared or wanted to suggest that they share the hard-earned sweet reward. Bob and Molly enjoyed it to the last sticky drop. Let me add that they did offer their parents each a taste but not their respective brother and sister!

I cannot remember whether it was two or three springs during which those two tapped trees for sap. However, the above was the climax of such endeavors and it was 1917. With the United States in the war and Steve's increasing lack of attention to his business, I was led to putting my foot down for the first time. I said firmly, "This is the last summer we go to the Island." Then I added, "With Harriet and Katie's help I am sending Phyllis to a fine camp in Maine. She is sixteen and I hope to have her go to college in the autumn of 1918."

To this, Steve had no reply. I knew that great trouble was brewing—that it was chiefly financial—but knew no details. During that summer there were few vegetables from the once huge garden on the mainland. When I went over to see for myself, I was appalled at the state of disrepair of the entire farm. Scores of expensive fruit trees which Steve had planted were dying from lack of care and water. The farm house looked deserted. However, the dogs on the Island were being cared for.

The summer passed pleasantly but I missed Phyllis. However, her letters were ecstatic about the Luther Gulick camp and all the new friends she was making among her own age group. We obviously could have little company but Molly still enjoyed her swimming and sailing the canoe. She was still enough of a solitary soul so that she didn't appear to miss companionship. However, she spent far more time reading. I had always taken many library books to the Island and both girls had developed a real love of reading. Now, Molly, approaching puberty, was devouring books of all kinds, which delighted me.

Toward the end of the summer I realized that Steve was practically never going into town, that most of his time spent away from the Island was spent in traveling about in his old, beat-up Ford, going to see the farmers who had his dogs. I faced him.

"Have you lost your job at the Radford Company?"

"Well, yes, in a way. Charlie (his older brother), the dirty dog, froze me out."

I was, of course, indignant at this treachery but had an intuition that there was much I didn't know. I asked, "How long since you've been to the office?"

"Oh, most of the summer, I guess."

"What have we been living on?"

"Savings," he replied.

"Mine, too?"

"Well, it was ours, wasn't it?"

"And the mortgage you got me to sign a year ago 'for a good investment'—is that paid back?"

With that Steve put on his hat and left for a hike.

I said no more but got busy packing everything usable for the last time. I hadn't the heart to tell Molly that we wouldn't be coming back. When we were back in town Phyllis returned and went happily back to high school for her last year and Molly started her last year at the fine Normal School with Bob, as usual.

Early that fall a mysterious fire broke out at that school one night. Being a lumber town, Oshkosh had many bad fires. This was especially spectacular as the old building was of brick and the walls stood as columns of flame poured out of every window. We all went down to see it. Steve always went to fires and Molly usually went with him. One firehouse with its magnificent white horses was just two blocks from our home and Molly knew all the firemen and their equipment, including, of course, how to slide down their pole. This fire, although a terrific sight, was a sobering experience. Steve was an active member of the school board—had been for years.

Although, traditionally, school kids are said to be delighted when their school burns down, I don't think Molly was. Two days later I discovered that she had, unseen, crept into her room at school which was in a part which was not completely gutted, and rescued her favorite book—*Poems Every Child Should Know*. I was aghast when I found out about it.

The fire had taken place on a Friday morning. Most children envisioned several weeks' vacation. However, I was proud when our small town turned to and with the cooperation of other schools, but chiefly all the churches in town, all

23

our children were able to resume their classes the following Monday morning.

The end result seemed to be, in our case at least, greater interest in school. Molly, and I think Robert, both did better work. Molly did much more homework although she was still far from a top student. She still didn't lack for out-of-doors life and Steve was always taking several children on hikes, canoe trips on the rivers, etc. He taught them much about nature—wild flowers, birds, etc. All he said to me in those days was that he had a really Big Deal on and everything would come out all right.

Late in the spring Robert and Molly embarked on their last childhood adventure. Although the war really touched none of us, the two were interested in what they heard about trenches and dugouts. They decided that they'd have their own dugout. With mansized picks and shovels they started in the Osborns' back yard, under the clothes line. None of us adults dreamed they'd keep at it for long but were glad the youngsters were well occupied in the fresh air and well within sight of both houses.

To our astonishment, the two kept at this really tough job most of the summer. When a hole six feet square and six feet deep was finished they lined the walls with slabs of wood with the bark still on (purloined from the Osborns' basement). On one side wall they had dug out a good-sized niche for a fireplace from which they had erected an old stove pipe. They built a small table and bench, implanting the legs in the dirt floor. The roof of the little room was made of more slabs, with only a small hatchway for entrance. Robert and Molly shoveled the excavated dirt back over the roof, making a large, rather unsightly hump. The two then took their small savings from saved allowances of ten cents a week and visited the Ten-Cent Store. There they bought a few doll-sized kitchen utensils; knives, forks, spoons, etc. They celibrated their completed "home" by eating their own cooked meal without suffocating from smoke! No adult could get in or out of the dugout but all did peer through the hatch and marveled.

With nothing further to do to it the boy and girl, like most people, lost interest in it. However, they would allow no one

24

to fill it in or destroy it. Fall and winter came. School and other interests took their attention. The war was over. The dugout was filled with water by spring—but Robert and Molly had their way. The hump was leveled, the little "home" was filled in as it was—nothing was removed. It remains for future archeologists to puzzle over the small dishes and other findings at some distant date!

END OF CHILDHOOD

CHAPTER II. GROWING UP

Change

(MARY)

What was I going to do? By this time I felt that I finally had to be on my own. The family was bound to break up. All I wanted to live for was my children's future. Phyllis was all right. She had returned to camp in Maine for the second summer. She had done so well the first year that she was asked back as a junior counselor which meant that she earned half her expenses. By giving up what little household help I had had, I managed to pay the rest. She was now in her first year at Vassar and was doing well. Much to my surprise, Steve paid her first semester's tuition.

"Where did you get that kind of money?" I asked incredulously.

"Oh, that big deal I told you about came through."

I didn't believe it but, being quite sure he was honest and could not have stolen it, I let the matter drop. I knew he would tell me no more and was grateful that Phyllis was actually in college. Fortunately, Molly was still mostly tomboy and I had none of the great worries some of my friends had over early teen-age daughters. Most of her friends were boys still but the relationships were healthy. Weekends were given over to hiking, skating, and canoeing, sometimes with Steve and often not.

Later Steve bought a safe old saddle horse which he pastured at the farm west of town where the collies now were. The summer when Molly was fourteen she was ecstatic as she had always longed to learn to ride. Steve wisely insisted that she learn to ride old Pet bareback with just a halter. She also had to take a trolley car to the end of the line and then walk to the farm over a mile from there. She further had to go out in the pasture call the horse to her, and climb on him. At first, naturally, Steve or the man who took care of the dogs supervised and helped her. However, she soon showed that she could manage by herself and it was a proud day when she was allowed to leave the farm on Pet, who by then had a second-hand saddle and bridle.

She knew all the surrounding farmers and their families; there were no paved roads and practically no cars on them. Furthermore, in those distant days one didn't have to worry about vandals, thugs, rapists, kidnappers, or murderers—at least in that rural, God-fearing, and hard-working area. With her beloved horse and one pet collie who always went with her, she was once more the rather solemn, self-sufficient soul who didn't need much human companionship. I thanked heaven that she had fewer accidents and illnesses which had plagued some of her earlier years.

As for myself, I had increasingly worse hay fever which was developing into bad bouts of asthma. As I look back I am quite sure much of this had a psychological basis but certainly I had numerous allergies (as they would be called today), also. I was alone with my tangled thoughts most of the time and slept badly. I did a minimum of necessary housework, read omniverously, and wrote letters to my sister Hat and my cousin Catherine in Chicago. They were the only ones to whom I could tell my problems.

Steve would seldom talk, when home, except about his nature walks. If any unpleasant subject arose he would put on his hat and leave the house. I tried to keep my letters to Phyllis cheerful. She, naturally, had much to write and tell about her new life at college, and she continued to do well in her studies. However, when she came home for Christmas (she spent her other vacations with friends), she sensed the strained atmosphere and knew trouble was brewing. I was happy that she had a few beaux in Oshkosh and Neenah (at the north end of the lake) who took her to dances, etc.

By the summer of 1920 I had decided that Molly should go to the camp in Maine with Phyllis, who was then to be a senior counselor and earn her entire keep. This would allow me to give my entire time to working out our future. My sister Hattie, who was then Mrs. C. D. Dallas, had three small children and was living in Winnetka, north of Chicago. She had generously offered to take Molly into her home the following year. There Molly would attend the fine North Shore Country Day School and be able to prepare for college. By that time the finer colleges were demanding Comprehensive Entrance Examinations which required far more rigorous work than the local Oshkosh High School was demanding (especially from a rather mediocre student which Molly still was).

We were lucky, extremely so, in finding the remarkable Luther Gulick camp, Sebago-Wohelo, in Maine. In my wide reading I had found that there were a few such places for girls. I had even answered a couple of advertisements. However, on a trip to Chicago to see my sister and cousin to discuss my increasingly serious home problems I happened to meet a fine woman who told me all about the Gulick camp which her daughter was still attending. The upshot was that I sent Phyllis there and later Molly. Both girls continued to go there for many summers over a period of about fourteen years. No one could write about these experiences except one who had been there as a camper. In later years Molly wrote the following account.

Camp

(MOLLY)

Phyllis's glowing accounts of her summers in Maine probably gave me the first and only feeling of envy toward my sister. By 1920 she was not only a very Senior Counselor, but was also given the job of chaperoning the quite large contingent of Midwestern girls who were then going to the same camp. It was the first time and only time, I think, that I was "under my sister's thumb." As I recall, I didn't behave too badly. I was thrilled at the prospect and proud my sister was in charge. I had never been on an overnight train and had never been with so many strangers.

The trip took two days and nights to Boston. There we

were joined by hordes of other girls and boys and took the old Boston and Maine Railway to Sebago Lake. From there we went by boat across the beautiful lake to the three camps. In those days the Gulicks had a camp for small boys at Panther Pond, not far from Sebago, and two separate ones for small girls and older girls on the shores of Sebago—a gorgeous setting of rocks, evergreen trees, and beaches strung along the crystal clear water's edge.

It was all glorious. We lived in tents, four in each, one of whom was a counselor. I had an edge on many of the city girls in that I was already at home in and on the water. Also I had the advantage over many others in having learned to ride a horse with considerable assurance, though definitely lacking in style. My country background stood me in good stead when it came to cooking out-of-doors, enjoying storms and various aspects of nature. I had even learned to make a bed, albeit not a very good or neat one!

On the other side of the coin, I was not at all accustomed to living with other people aside from my family. In the summer months I had had practically no routine to follow as was certainly necessary in a group of some eighty-odd girls.

None of this did I realize or appreciate at age fifteen. However, I loved it all. I learned to swim and dive in proper form as well as to ride a horse in acceptable fashion. I even learned to make a neat bed and keep my corner of the tent in order. The activities, none of which was compulsory for anyone, included many other things, most of which one usually didn't get in school. There were nature walks, studying birds, wild flowers, ferns, and trees, as well as many small animals. I had been accustomed to such hikes all my life but many of the birds, animals, and plant life of Maine were different from those of the Midwest, so were of real interest to me.

What I had never encountered were the arts and crafts-—most of them based on American Indian arts. There were classes in pottery and weaving, bead work and jewelry. The latter consisted of working in copper, and the more accomplished artisans were allowed to work in silver, turquoise, etc. Instead of school-type competitive sports, there were opportunities for interpretive dancing and drama, aside from the many varieties of water sports.

A nondenominational Sunday service was held each week in a semi-open building on a point across the bay. Mrs. Gulick (her Indian name which everyone used in speaking with or about her was Hiitini) was a remarkable and lovable woman who, with her late husband, had started the camp in 1908 for their own family and friends. She was also the founder of the Camp Fire Girls. Her down-to-earth philosophy was based on Work, Health, and Love. The camp was named Sebago WOHELO for these three important aspects of life. The simple religious service plus Monday night camp fires were inspirations to all who went to camp. These were held on the tennis court.

The girls sat crosslegged on the ground in a triangle (the symbol of Work, Health, and Love). A large camp fire was laid in the center. Mrs. Gulick (Hiitini) would walk up to this, kneel, and start *making* fire. This was done as American Indians had done it for centuries. The equipment was simple and homemade. It consisted of a more or less rigid bow of ash (I believe). To each end of this was attached the ends of a slack thong of rawhide. A spindle of cedar (?) was inserted into a loop of the thong. One end of the spindle, a sharp point, was placed in a small hole bored near the edge of a balsam plank. From the hole to the edge of the plank a notch had been cut. Nearby was a small pile of finely shredded cedar shavings.

The "fire maker" placed one knee on the plank, inserted the point of the spindle into the hole and drew the bow back and forth rapidly and steadily, making the spindle whirl in the balsam hole. As the wood dust gathered it fell down the notch onto a piece of metal beneath it. The friction finally created enough heat to produce a tiny glowing coal in the gathering wood dust. At this point Hiitini lifted the glowing dust around which, with her other hand, she cupped some of the cedar shavings. Then, with slow, deep breaths she blew on the small pile which sooner or later burst into flame. From this she lighted an oil-soaked torch. In an impressive ritual she lighted each of five torches held in the hands of the Head Counselors who, in turn, thrust their flames into the ready-stacked wood. The evening performance began.

This consisted usually of small plays, written, stage-designed, and performed by the camp girls. There was ballet dancing, singing, etc. In fact, much of camp life was built around song. Practically all the girls sang at their work, their play, their religious observances, and any other time they felt like it. Most of these songs were written by the counselors and girls and were sung from year to year, each year adding new ones. They were inspirational, comic, patriotic, absurd, and narrative in ballad form—all kinds.

Memories of all of this, especially the music, have stayed with me all the fifty-odd years since. I was fortunate enough in my childhood years to have had some music instruction at the Normal School and also to be able to carry a tune. I never had a good voice or learned how to play any instrument. However, I was periodically exposed to fine music during my life and because any sort of song which is tuneful appeals to me I still sing at work or play and remember almost all tunes and words I've learned over the years.

The song, "Without a Song," by Gershwin, I believe, exemplifies a good deal of my philosophy in life.

Challenge I

(MARY)

Before Molly went to Winnetka to live with the Dallases I just happened to hear through a chance acquaintance that Steve's Big Deal was a real one. He had promoted a proposition to build a good-sized sugar beet processing plant in Wisconsin (the first one, I believe). His promotion was acted upon, the plant was built and became successful. Steve received $20,000 for his part in the deal. He had never told me a word about it and had banked the money in Milwaukee. When I did, belatedly, hear about it I confronted him with the fact, stating,

"Now I can see how you managed some of Phyllis's tuition. I trust you have paid off the mortgage and other debts."

"Well," he admitted, "some of them"

"Is there any of the $20,000 left?"

"Yes, some."

32

It was futile for me to try to get any more details, but I did say, "Harriet told me just recently that you had borrowed quite a bit from her some years ago. Have you repaid that?"

Knowing, of course, that I could easily check on that, he admitted that he hadn't. My succinct reply was that if he had *any* love at all for Molly (he had always insisted she was the light of his life), "You will pay Harriet all you owe her at once. She and Don are prepared to pay all of her living and tuition for the next two years as well as have her live with them. This will give her the chance to get into a good college and make something of her life. If you don't pay that debt at once I shall cancel all those plans and Molly can clerk in the Ten-Cent Store for her living."

He paid that debt very shortly.

After a second year for Molly at camp, when she was sixteen she moved to Winnetka in the fall of 1921. During previous years I had interested myself in the Women's Suffrage movement. I had been unable to take a very active part physically in it. I was always strapped for money and needed most of my waking hours to keep the home running. I didn't even have the cash to pay for a hired girl to help with the housework, or for someone to do the laundry. I remember that more than once Molly came home from high school to find me scrubbing floors or ironing sheets, and asked why I didn't have some help. I had put her off by saying the girl was sick and couldn't come. Molly responded to this with only a question in her eyes. I couldn't bear to burden her with the whole tale until she was at least sixteen or seventeen.

I was happy to be able to contribute to the women's cause by writing articles, etc. I was rewarded for this by being sent to the Republican Convention in Chicago in 1920. Though my choice for the nomination was Leonard Wood and not Mr. Harding, the short trip did me good.

When both Molly and Phyllis were away from home I spent much more time in women's politics and writing for publications involved in them. Steve was seldom at home. Most of the time, as far as I knew, he was hiking over the countryside with neighboring children or taking them on canoe trips. In the spring he would get them to go out to the mainland property across from the Island and they would happily gather buckets of daffodils. In previous years he had ordered hundreds of bulbs from Holland at about the same time that he planted his large fruit orchards. The fruit trees, of course, had long since died but the daffodils had gone native and continued to bloom over acres of land—a beautiful sight but not exactly a cash crop. Those which were picked were either given away to all and sundry or allowed to "wither in the basement air" like "Rose of Washington Square."

By 1923 I had discovered that Steve had illegally taken a second mortgage on our home without my signature! He couldn't borrow anything on the Island property as it was in such a state of disrepair. I had frequently begged him to sell it. Most of my own money had gone into it but he held the major part of the stock and refused to even try to find a buyer, saying, "Oh, it is too lovely a place and soon all will be well and we'll be able to go back!"

At this point there was no "going back" for me! Not in any sense of the word. Molly had been entered in Mount Holyoke College and had passed her entrance examinations. That summer she had gone to a camp in northern Wisconsin, instead of Maine, as she could earn more money as the head and fully qualified swimming instructor even though she was only eighteen.

I spent most of that summer sorting out and packing my belongings—or at least all that I could take with me. I announced to Steve that I was leaving. I was going East with Molly when she went to college and would get myself a job in New York. Phyllis by then had graduated from Vassar and had a very nice job teaching at the Monte-Mare School at Lake Placid. This school spent the coldest months in Miami, Florida. I could at least be with my girls for vacation and a number of weekends.

Steve looked glum and said he saw no reason why I should want to do such a thing. Want? It was all I *could* do! The previous winter our electricity had been turned off because the bills weren't paid. The coal company had refused to deliver furnace fuel for the same reason.

34

I did say that I would leave for one year, then return. If by that time he had paid up *any* of his large bills and had managed to keep just himself, I would try once more. He didn't believe me. However, when the time came and Molly and I actually left, bag and baggage, he seemed stunned. Most of our friends were, too, as none of them knew anything about the situation. Marital separation and/or divorce were not usual in those days, especially in a small town.

Molly went to South Hadley and I found a tiny apartment in New York to share with another woman. I got a job (my first, at age 49) with the American Women's Club and was a free, but desperately lonely woman except for the times my girls could be with me.

Challenge II

(HARRIET)

Perhaps it is time for me to take over part of these recollections. Thanks to our dear mother, Louise Hughes, my sister Mary, and I had remained very close. We were as different from each other as Phyllis and Molly are. Also our lives, after growing up, were totally different. I had gone to college at the University of Wisconsin and had taken a Master's Degree at the University of Chicago. When I had taught school in Oshkosh for a few years I had lived with Mary and Steve and their girls in the early 1900s.

Most people admired Steve Radford and thought that Mary at age twenty had made a fine marriage. He had charm, came from a respected and comfortably-off family, and was certainly intelligent and well read. During the years that I lived with them I learned to love Phyllis and Molly and grieved with Mary over the loss of John. I did know that Steve had been very much spoiled by his mother and especially by his two unmarried sisters. (He was one of the youngest of nine children.) He was seven years older than Mary, eleven years my senior. Except for knowing that he was inclined to be quite self-righteous, if I had any further ideas about him in those early years it was that he was a fine father and a solid citizen.

I married C. Donald Dallas of Chicago in 1909 and left Oshkosh for good. Mary and I kept in close touch by letter and occasional visits but I knew little of her growing problems in the early teens. My life was taken up by my three small children and by my husband who was becoming a very fine businessman. Gradually Mary's letters bothered me more and more. Also, our cousin Catherine Cleveland, who was unmarried and like a sister to us both, told me that she knew there was serious trouble brewing in the Radford household. We both helped her financially at various times and had her visit in Chicago as often as possible.

When Mary had about reached the breaking point Don and I offered to take Molly into our home to finish her secondary education in Winnetka where we then lived. When Molly arrived after a summer's camping in Maine she was a healthy, happy, and normal sixteen-year-old who was belatedly emerging from a tomboy into a nice, rather quiet young woman. She fitted into the household very well and started in at our fine school with enthusiasm. She liked her teachers and her classmates and walked my two school-age youngsters, Hughes and Louise, to school each day.

I suspected that by then she knew that things were not going at all well at home, but she and I seldom discussed anything touching on the subject. However, Catherine and I had both tentatively urged Mary to leave Steve, and thought she would do so before long. Meanwhile we were getting used to having a budding young lady as part of the family.

It didn't take long before a handsome young man, Willoughby Walling, began to be much in evidence around the place. A bit later he was arriving at the front door along with the morning paper well ahead of time to walk Molly to school. He had a younger sister and two brothers and was most tolerant of my children. In fact my two-year-old baby Mary adored him. Bill, as he wanted to be called, helped our two, Hughes and Louise, into their snow suits and the four of them set off for school. Romance was certainly in the offing!

Molly readily accepted our ruling that on school nights she

was not expected to go out. On weekends she could go out but was expected to return home by eleven o'clock and she was entrusted with a house key. Clearly, this seemed reasonable to us and for the most part the rules were observed. What did surprise us was that she was so level-headed at that age, particularly with such an impetuous and attractive, as well as persistent "beau!" On many week nights Bill would beg, borrow, or just take his family's car, a beautiful Marmon, and drive around and around our block. This apparently did not affect Molly seriously but I must admit that on occasion it did us! Sometimes we felt so sorry for the enamored boy that we would tell Molly to go out and talk with him, which she gladly did. Obviously she was not desperately in love with him.

I decided that this was understandable although my husband did not see eye-to-eye with me. Molly was quite a lot like me in many ways—I had been a tomboy in my earlier years and was late in acquiring very romantic feelings. Molly was so accustomed to playing with boys that she just naturally enjoyed their company as people and as friends. For some time she accepted this adoration without seeming to be flattered by it or getting overly excited by it. Most of the young people we knew in those days were well brought up and didn't try to "kick over the traces." Even Bill, enamored as he was, showed far more restraint than young people of later years.

Their relationship was also held in bounds by the fact that these two enjoyed hiking, swimming, skating, and many other healthy outdoor activities which certainly helped to sublimate more wildly emotional tendencies. For all of these, we and Mary were most grateful. What we semi-Victorians would have done with such a situation in the very permissive later years we couldn't imagine! In any case, Bill took out many of his emotions and frustrations by writing reams of poetry and making, with his own hands, lovely gifts for Molly.

We all, including his parents, were quite relieved when the young man went off to Cornell. Molly was persuaded by her teachers, also Mary and me, to take one more year of preparatory school in Winnetka before trying for her college board exams. Hence the romantic pressure let up and Molly got down to her studies more seriously. She also had more time for other friends, and seemed contented enough but she continued to get—so she told me—impassioned letters from Bill for some two or three years afterwards.

College

(MARY)

After Molly returned from the Wisconsin camp in the fall of 1923 and had been accepted in Mount Holyoke she and I went East together, and as I stated previously I got my job in New York. Molly hated college except for the lovely countryside thereabouts. She managed to pass her courses, with a condition in Latin. She continued her outdoor activities; skating, swimming, and hiking with various semi-serious beaux from nearby Amherst, and went in strongly for all athletics. Every time there was the slightest opportunity to get away, she would come to see me in New York. Once, to my astonished concern, she hitchhiked with her roommate, as her allowance wasn't big enough to allow for the fare. She would usually arrive in the city with a nickel in her pocket to pay for subway fare to reach my modest quarters.

Those weekends and especially longer vacations when Phyllis could join us from Monte-Mare were a delight to us all. I saved up for them and we spent much of the time in gallery seats at the theatre—Charlot's Revue, the "Little Shows," the Theatre Guild plays, musicales of the day, etc. When it came time for Molly to return to college she would apologetically say that she didn't have money for the train fare. Determined as I was that she should continue college, begging her to try one more semester, I would dig up the money and she would go back.

By the fall of 1924, dear Cousin Catherine offered Phyllis the money to go to graduate school at Columbia. She felt that the latter had earned her living for two years and was entitled to further study for which she was so keen. I was delighted, of course, as it meant that we could live together in New York. In the meantime, with both girls earning their summer living at camp, I returned home as I had promised Steve I would do.

There I found that in spite of his protestations he had been thoroughly enjoying his carefree, bachelor living. He not only had not paid any of his debts but had acquired many new ones. I thereupon packed up everything which was legally mine in the house, stored the things with friends and relatives, and got a Legal Separation. I never went back to Oshkosh until I learned that Steve had gone East to live with his oldest spinster sister, Elizabeth, who never ceased to adore him. He lived with and on her from then on. As an aside—some time later all my old friends had found out the facts. Many of them had their eyes opened when they found that there was no hope of retrieving the money they had loaned him!

Molly, I am thankful to say, did better in her sophomore year at college. She had taken an elective course in biology which fascinated her. Her professor was excellent and inspired her to really get down to studying. We three, again, enjoyed theaters, concerts, etc. together and I had a better job. Things were really looking up and I felt enormous relief from possible responsibility for any more debts. In fact, by the next summer, with Hattie's and Katie's help I took Phyllis to Europe. Her college roommate went with us. I felt that I had achieved a good part of my ambition—one of my daughters had had a good education—she was asked back to Columbia for a part-time teaching job and a chance to finish her Master's Degree thesis. Now she was to have a chance for some travel before she looked for a real job and would be more tied down. Both girls had numerous beaux during this period but nothing apparently serious except for one of Molly's. That, Hattie will have to tell about.

East to West

(HARRIET)

When Mary and Phyllis went to Europe in the summer of 1925, Don and I had decided to take our children to Wyoming. We invited Molly to go with us instead of teaching swimming at camp. At that time Molly was with us after college and she seemed to be really in love with an attractive, wealthy Chicago man, quite a bit older than she. She had met him during the previous Christmas vacation which she had spent with us. Ray had given her quite a rush—theaters, dancing at the Drake, and rubbing shoulders with more or less "high society" in the city. She appeared to be quite a grown-up young lady. However, her tomboy propensities still lingered on and produced rather disastrous results for her. After skating at the Indian Hill Country Club one day she had taken off her skating boots, and near the clubhouse she saw a toboggan slide. There were a few young people who were trying out skis on this slide. She should have known better but couldn't resist putting on a pair of skis over her bedroom slippers and galoshes and tackling something she'd never done before. The snow on the slide had partly melted, one ski struck bare wood, and Molly ended up with four broken metatarsals!

Of course she was in a cast for the rest of the holiday, and her beau found other more ladylike partners to dance with. We thought she was brokenhearted when she returned to college. However, by summer when she returned to us she appeared to have recovered from her great love and went happily to the J-Y Ranch in Wyoming with us. This was a gorgeous place situated on the shores of a beautiful small lake at the foot of the Grand Tetons. On reaching there after a complicated train and motor journey via Idaho we were all charmed and delighted with the place. Molly, however, really fell in love with the West at that time and never got over it.

It was a lovely summer, with swimming, much riding, and camping trips up to eleven thousand feet. The place was wonderfully run and the countryside was completely un-spoiled by tourists, crowded roads, and people in general. The other guests were delightful and made up mostly of families, so there were many children. Some from eastern cities had never known such free, outdoor life before. One day Molly asked one of the Boston children who had driven all the way out, what route they had taken.

The astonishing reply from this city boy was, "Oh, we took the Old Post Road!"

Emily Johnson, our wonderful helper who stayed with us for thirty-five years, was with us and took perfect care of lit-tle Mary who was just six then. Molly was very good with the numerous other youngsters, teaching them to swim, helping them to learn to ride, and generally keeping them occupied while the grown-ups were busy at their own pur-suits. Her experience as counselor at the Gulick camp stood her in very good stead and she made such an impression on Henry Stewart, the owner and manager of the ranch, that he asked her to come back the next summer, free of charge, if she would act as junior hostess for the youngsters. We were all delighted, and made definite reservations to return the next summer.

One highlight of that summer of 1925 was the watching of the building of that remarkable log church in the Snake River Valley not too far below the ranch. We all made fre-quent trips by car or horseback to watch its progress. It has been written up, described, and photographed so many times in the intervening years and been seen by so many thousands in what is now Grand Teton National Park that it needs no description here. It was an inspiration to see it go up log by log, with the local ranchers doing all the work. It was also a great privilege, we thought, to attend the opening service of that church conducted by the then Bishop of Wyoming. None of us ever forgot it.

Molly definitely remembers it as the most impressive house of worship that she ever visited all over the world.

CHAPTER III. RETURN TO THE MIDWEST

New Life

(MARY)

The year of 1926-1927 was a definite turning point in our three lives. Molly astonished me by deciding that she wanted to study medicine. Here was my child who had always been indifferent toward school, hated her early days at college, and was, at best, a mediocre student —wanting to take on years more of study! During her freshman mathematics course her professor, Miss Hazlett, had once told her (she stuttered badly),

"M-M-Miss R-Radford, I wish y-y-you w-w-would be w-with us m-more often; you have a g-good h-head f-for figures and s-s-should g-g-g-get m-much better g-g-grades."

Molly in astonishment replied, "Why, Miss Hazlett, I don't think I have ever cut one of your classes!"

"N-no, I d-d-don't mean th-that. Y-you are with us in b-b-body b-b-but n-not in sp-sp-p-pirit."

Now with her new determination she changed from her major in English literature and tackled higher mathematics, chemistry, and physics, as well as biology. Chemistry was especially difficult for her. Although she passed that subject, her professor told her in no uncertain terms that she would never be a scientist and had no hope of studying medicine. That simply made Molly dig in and she stubbornly refused to be deterred.

In the spring she decided she wanted to transfer to the University of Chicago where she knew she could get better pre-medical preparation. This coincided beautifully with

Phyllis's and my plans. Phyllis had just been offered a fine job with the Quaker Oats Company in Chicago. Her specialty by then was in health education, and the forward-looking company wanted a health consultant in its advertising department. This was a brand new approach in business in those days and Phyllis was to form and build up her department from scratch—a real challenge.

So, in the fall, we three were back in Chicago. There I would be near my favorite uncle, J. J. Dau who had taken me in when I was seventeen. His wife, my much loved Aunt Harriet, had died. Cousin Catherine was running his handsome home for him. Also, the apartment we three found on the near north side was very close to my old school friends, Marie Clark Smith and May Merryweather. We had never lost touch but had seen little of one another in many years. Molly obtained a ride to the south side with a fellow student—we had no car in those days—and took up her studies in earnest.

Another joy was to be relatively near my sister Harriet and her family in Winnetka. We were often out in that lovely suburb for weekends, which offered a fine change from city life. This extended period until the Dallas family moved to New York in 1932 brought Harriet and me as close together as our mother could have wished. My only worry was Molly's determination to study medicine. I couldn't afford to send her through four more years of school and I honestly didn't believe she was strong enough to go through that vigorous course. However, I hoped against hope that when she got her Bachelor's Degree she might change her mind —perhaps even stick to one beau and get married!

My hopes were vain! My grown-up Molly could be as single-tracked and stubborn as she often was as a child. When she returned from a summer in Maine in 1927 after she had acquired her B.S. degree, she plunked down her summer earnings for a small room over a gift shop near the medical school and for her first quarter's tuition. Then, with a club friend, Frances Owen, who had the room next to her, got a job in the women's cafeteria where they prepared breakfasts between 5 AM and 7 AM. In return the girls earned all they could eat, three meals a day.

44

Molly got a job with the director of women's athletics teaching swimming, field hockey, and basketball in the appropriate seasons, and during "off hours" from her courses. This paid for future room rent, books (medical books didn't come cheap), and extras. Her third job, which I didn't hear about until later, was at night, making microscopic slides in one of the laboratories. She had learned this technique in a microbiology course she'd taken the previous years. This would earn tuition for future quarters.

When I asked her about cost of clothing she replied, "I'll just wear what I have and worry about new ones when present ones wear out!"

When she did her studying for her difficult courses in anatomy, chemistry, and bacteriology I never did know. What I do know is that despite working what seemed to be a twenty-five-hour day eight days a week, she and Frances always managed to get jobs ushering at the theater and acting as "supers" in the Chicago Civic Opera. Thus she managed to see most of the good plays and be in or see and hear many of the fine operas that came to Chicago in those pre-Depression days. For an inveterate sleeper, how she got along with next to no rest I'll never know! As long as she stayed healthy and happy I was content. Phyllis was doing very well in her new and interesting job and all was "right with the world" for the three of us.

NEW WORLD

In the spring of 1928 our dear Cousin Katie died of cancer. She left her entire estate (which was considerable from my point of view) to me. I was, for the first time in my life, financially independent. I happily went to take over Katie's job as companion and housekeeper for my favorite uncle. From a penniless Danish immigrant boy he had risen to the head of Ried-Murdoch, a successful wholesale grocery firm. His handsome home on the south side of Chicago (not the one I had lived in with him and dear Aunt Harriet when I was a school girl) was not too far from the University and was well staffed with a fine cook, a maid, and a chauffeur.

What a change from any of my former life! Uncle was a

45

darling, personally, as well as being extremely well read and a joy to be with, even in his advancing years. Soon after moving in with him I began to plot in Molly's behalf.

Katie had left each of my girls a bequest of five thousand dollars. I began to read travel advertisements. Soon I found just the thing. A "Floating University" was being formed and was to sail the following autumn for a round-the-world cruise of almost ten months. It was to be made up of about one hundred students and ten professors and would offer a year's college credit to the students who were lucky enough to be enrolled and who had the cash—twenty-five hundred to four thousand dollars!

It didn't take me long to present this wonderful proposition to Molly. "You have Katie's bequest, this is your chance to travel—perhaps the best and only one while you are still young enough to get the most out of it."

"Well, it sounds wonderful but I still have more than three years of medical school ahead of me."

"That is true," I said, secretly hoping that such a year *might* alter the future plan entirely. "However, I know for certain that the education from travel will make any future you choose more interesting and worthwhile." I added, "Also, now that I have the wherewithall, I shall be glad to finance the rest of your course, if and when you want to continue when you get back."

It didn't take long for Molly to apply and be accepted by this odd university. Having her college degree, she wouldn't need the credits, but we were both sure that she would benefit as much if not more than other students from the courses she chose to take.

Years later, Molly wrote up her experiences of that year, based on her letters home which I kept. She will take over the next part of this screed.

CHAPTER IV

Nine-Hour Luncheon

(MOLLY)

Twenty-five years later (1954) there was to be a reunion of the "Floating University." During the planning of this get-together I received a long list of names and addresses of the members of that long-ago trip. Since I was headed east to meet mother who was returning from England, I wrote my former "boyfriend," Addy Mueller, who was then a law professor at Yale. I asked him if he was planning to attend the reunion. He replied, probably not, but since I was to be in New York would I have lunch with him on a given Friday and we would have our own reunion. I promptly accepted the invitation.

The following chapter I wrote in 1955 while awaiting the publication of my only book, BILL MARTIN, AMERICAN, first printed by The Caxton Press, Idaho, now being reprinted by the Vantage Press, New York. The letters were, of course, written in 1928-29 when I was 23 to 24 years old.

It was a hot summer day on the New York streets but in the air-conditioned Pierre a middle-aged couple sat comfortably at a corner table. The luncheon crowd had not yet started to come in, and the waiter, after bringing the drinks, stood off to one side.

"Where does one begin after twenty-five years?" she said, "Tell me about your family—and how did you happen to leave the business world for your profession?"

"My daughter is a senior at Wellesley, she's more or less

47

engaged. She looks like me, they say, but she's like her mother, thank goodness—she doesn't have my temperament. She loves horses! Can you imagine?"

"I do remember that, except for swimming, you didn't care much for the outdoor sports—you weren't keen on riding those little Chinese ponies in Canton. How old is your son? What is he like?"

"He's fifteen and at boarding school. Poor devil, he's like me, inside, but he looks like his mother—I have a picture here.

"But tell me, Molly, after you got your M. D. degree how did you happen to get all the way out to the Southwest?"

"Well, I went out for a ten-day vacation in 1936. I loved it, so I never came back except to pack up my belongings."

"You ended up doing what you wanted to, didn't you? Living the kind of life you wanted?"

"Yes, and you did too; surely it seems to me you've reached the top in your profession."

"Well, maybe—but where does one go from here? Do you remember, I was always restless—never quite satisfied?"

"That's probably why you got where you are. It must have taken a lot of courage to leave a settled business and go back to school. I take my hat off to you."

"It didn't take any courage, really—I had financial security for my family. If I had failed to make the grade I could have gone back to the business.

"Tell me, what sort of man did you marry?"

"He was short and homely. Our backgrounds were entirely different. It was an exciting and strenuous few years—but they were happy ones and it was all too short."

"Do you remember when we landed at Kobe that you and I took adjoining rooms at the hotel when the rest of the gang stayed on board that night?"

"Good Lord, did we? How can you remember?"

"I remember a lot. I can even remember the name of your first beau, when you were sixteen—long before we met!"

"I'll bet you kept a diary and you've looked at it recently. I never did or could keep any kind of a journal. If I'd known before coming East this trip that all this was going to happen, I would have dug out the letters my family saved for

me. I don't think I have read them for over twenty years. I'm
sure I still have them stored away somewhere."

* * * * *

On Board S.S. President Wilson
November 10, 1928

Mother, darling:

Classes started today, but as I have none scheduled for
Saturday until three o'clock, I now have plenty of time to
write the first letter of the trip.

I am glad you left the pier when you did the other day as
it was so wet and rainy. Actually the ship didn't sail until
4:30. Fortunately the fog had lifted by the time we got out
into the river, so we could see quite a lot as we sailed out of
the harbor. The fact that it was almost dark made it even
nicer—for all the lighted windows of New York made it look
like a fairy city, all the outlines of which were indistinct.

Up until today it has been quite cold but we are now far
enough south to have very mild air. We are in the trough of
the waves, on the edge of some storm,* so the ship rolls a lot
and makes some people feel queer; in fact, quite a lot of
them. I seem to have no such feelings; in fact, my appetite is
ravenous and my spirits splendid. I guess it will take a real
storm, if that, to make me seasick. I find myself quite mad
about the sea!

The people are, for the most part, very nice. The students
seem very young. So far I have been getting acquainted
mostly with the older people. The art instructor who is taking Holling's place is an interesting woman of the world,
Lucille Douglas. I am glad she is my advisor.

*The storm in which the Vestriss sank.

* * * * *

S.S. President Wilson
November 13, 1928

Mother, dear:

We left Havana at midnight last night after quite a delightful day. We landed yesterday morning and were royally
received by a flock of Cubans, most of whom came from the
University of Havana.

At luncheon, someone asked Jane George (of the "Single Tax" George family) and me if we'd like to go with a small party in one of the private cars, and, of course, we accepted. We were all to be taken about as guests of the reception committee—most of the others went in busses.

Jane and I found ourselves in a large Packard with the Director (President) of the University and the head Dean. There didn't seem to be room for any more in that car, for some reason, so the four of us, with chauffeur, started out. Both of our escorts spoke enough English so that we could get along, although we frequently lapsed into some French. They drove us all over the city, which is really beautiful and the cleanest place I've ever seen. It is built along the sea coast, with wide boulevards, perfectly kept parks, and promenades—a blue, blue sea and sky—and even the humblest of buildings looked artistic.

We went to the University and were the first to arrive. All the Cuban students gaped at us but they were delightfully hospitable. Whenever we passed a Cuban he stopped and removed his hat till we went by. (Great respect for the President and Dean?) Most of the University is newly built and a lovely, perfectly unified set of buildings.

Later we drove out into the country, all of which seemed like a lovely garden....We didn't see one eyesore. We went to a darling place for tea, or rather cocktails...where we looked out over a green-glazed dance floor which looked like ice. The daiquiri was excellent, the company stimulating, and the dance floor perfect!....

We arrived late at one of the many country clubs where the whole party was to be entertained at tea, but being in the most distinguished company, no one criticized. More music, predominantly Cuban this time, and much dancing. My Dean wasn't a bad dancer—better than Jane's President, I thought, and younger too. There we really drank tea.

We got permission from Mrs. G. to have dinner with "our" Cubans and dressed in our best left the ship's side about seven. Our escorts had the chauffeur fill our laps with masses of gorgeous gladioli. We then drove off through a soft, heavenly evening to what they claimed was the finest restaurant in Cuba.

The food and champagne were delicious and our hosts most complimentary. We had a private dining room—but there were four of us. Such lines as those Latins have! Never in my twenty-three years have I heard the like. "My" Ricardo swore eternal love to me right before the others. Both men used such extravagant terms to extoll our beauty, etc., that Jane and I had to laugh. Fortunately, both men had good senses of humor and we all ended up laughing together. . . .

They got us back to the ship just before sailing time and we dashed up the gangplank with our arms full of flowers, quite sure we would not forget Cuba and that one day there for a long time to come. . . .

We are headed for Panama. Meantime I'd better study a bit even though I'm working for no credits. . . .I feel especially lucky to be traveling now, at this age, and plan to use my study hours for learning all I can about the countries we are to visit.

S.S. President Wilson
November 17, 1928

Phyl, dear:

. . . .Going through the Panama Canal was a most impressive experience—such a wonderful piece of engineering! Most striking to me was the orderly way in which the whole thing was done. Gates in the locks opened and closed—hundreds of tons of water were let in or out with amazing speed and the ship moved on—all without an apparent order shouted or a word said. Luncheon was served on deck, so we could see all that went on. Although some were bored after we had gone through one or two locks, I was fascinated.

The countryside was hilly enough in places to be quite lovely and the luxuriance of the vegetation told us we were really in the tropics. The heat was fairly oppressive but there was enough breeze most of the time to make it bearable. . . .

* * * * *

The restaurant was crowded with people by now, but the couple in the corner were unaware of anything about them. For them, it wasn't New York in 1954, but a ship in 1928.

"Can you recall when we first met?"

51

"Not exactly, but we did sit at the same table fairly early in the trip, didn't we?"

"That's right but we didn't do Havana or California together."

"Or Honolulu, either, but I do remember the buggy ride in Panama—you, Fritz, and I."

The waiter appeared, bringing two drinks which he set on the table. After a brief glance at the man and the woman he replaced the menus under his arm and walked away.

"That 'flu bug we got in San Francisco cut us out of quite a few days before Hawaii—I don't remember much about that, do you?"

"Not too much except that I think I cared enough about you even then, to worry about you."

* * * * *

Aboard the S.S. President Wilson
November 19th, 1928

Dearest Family:

We got to Balboa about two o'clock and there left the ship for a few hours. I was with a most congenial group including John Decker, one of the younger instructors, Addy Mueller, and Fritz Jandrey. The two latter are Wisconsin boys who are just as nice as they can be. We drove over to Panama City, which can't compare in beauty with Havana but is in many ways much more interesting. In the old part of the city we saw some picturesque ruins of churches which had been built about 1540 and an amazing wide column of ants which crossed from one ruin to another. These creatures never stop going and coming and we are told no one ever expects to be able to stop them. . . .

We had Martinis for tea and then Fritz, Addy, and I hired a horse and buggy and drove back to the ship in a leisurely fashion. Fritz could speak some Spanish, so we got along fine with the driver. It was a perfect night, with a small moon over the Pacific and enough breeze to cool us off after a very hot day.

Our first daylight view of the new ocean as we sailed was lovely. The water was many shades of green and blue, under a vivid blue sky, and spotted with dark purple islands. Now

52

it is foggy and rainy and perhaps I'll get some studying done.

Later

This evening Addy and I went out to the bow for awhile. Two dolphins (or porpoises) appeared right at the prow, swimming directly ahead of us and near enough to the surface to be completely outlined in phosphorus. From time to time they leapt into the air, shaking sparks of greenish, golden light. This they repeated several times and then were joined by more of their pals. They all rushed through the sea ahead of us, leaving long trails of glowing phosphorus behind them—like comets in the water. Addy described them as "phantom spirits" guiding the ship through the night. . . .

Thank heaven both Addy and Fritz seem to feel much as I do about not talking too much or exclaiming at length over a lovely sight. I hope we three will be able to make a lot of expeditions together. . . .

Later

Somewhere off the coast of Nicaragua we hit the roughest weather so far. It was fairly exciting and hard to keep on one's feet. The windows on the promenade deck had to be opened wide to keep the smashing waves from breaking them. The wind came from our side, so portholes had to be kept closed—it was so stuffy in the cabin my two roommates and I finished the night sleeping on the deck.

At sea
(Day before Honolulu)

Mother darling:

The Wilson seems like home now and I think I'm going to hate leaving her in Japan. It's funny—I even resented seeing new people board the ship at San Francisco—she seems to be our own personal property. . . .Some of us have had the 'flu so haven't even done much studying. Now, thank goodness, we are on our feet and looking forward to Honolulu.

* * * * *

S.S. Wilson Friday
Don't know the date

Phyl, dear:

We are completely cut off from the rest of the world. No

53

one seems to exist but our fellow passengers. . . .

I do want to tell you about my day in Honolulu. I didn't go with the F.U. group. Mary Lois Pascal from camp met me. We drove to Queens Hospital which I wanted to see and looked up Paul Larssen—you remember the camp doctor of a couple of years ago? He was just as nice as ever and drove us about the Island. We called on Frances Gulick Jewett who is delightful. She is a charming frail little old lady who lives in a most picturesque home overlooking Waikiki and beyond to Diamond Head. We had a very pleasant visit with her and she was much interested to hear about camp. Incidentally one of the first things she said (in speaking of Hiitini's death) was,

"And who was the young lady who they said spoke so beautifully and so understandingly at the funeral services?"

I was proud to tell her that the young lady was my sister and that she had run the entire camp for the rest of the summer. . . .

The ship sailed at five and as we pulled out we lined up along the rail, laden with leis. The orchestra played Aloha Oe and dozens of colored serpentine streamers were thrown from shore and from ship. . . .

December 18

Just a week to Christmas, you were darling to send parcels to San Francisco.

* * * * *

The luncheon crowd had all gone and the waiters had cleared up the other tables. They were brushing up the last crumbs and straightening chairs.

"Six weeks on one ship with the same people wasn't quite the same as a transatlantic crossing or even a ten-day cruise, was it?"

"Hardly. By the time we got to Japan a very few people in the world existed for me, except you—and as I remember I didn't even have any mail from home for some time."

The man signaled to the waiter and ordered two more drinks.

"Japan, how beautiful it was—Kyoto for Christmas-

—Nikko at New Year's—no, not quite. But Shigisan—you haven't forgotten that?"

"No, I never forgot Shigisan—and I do remember quite a lot about Kyoto, too—but the details——?"

* * * * *

The Miyako Hotel
Kyoto, Japan
Dec. 22, 1928

Dearest family:

Just got off a cable which I hope will reach you for Christmas. The ship docked at Kobe about noon Thursday. Later Addy and I took a ricksha ride—it was fascinating to jog along through those narrow, lantern-lit streets and see the droves of Japanese clumping along on their wooden clogs. We had dinner at the Oriental Hotel and danced afterwards. We stayed at the hotel that night and returned to the ship the next morning for classes. Maybe there were some raised eyebrows, but we remembered all too well what it was like to try to sleep on shipboard when it was in port. In San Francisco the banging of loading and unloading was awful! After all, we did have separate rooms! When the time came to pack up and leave the ship I wasn't too sorry. Six weeks is a long time for three girls to live in one cabin the size of ours!

Kobe was comparatively drab and colorless—Osaka, which we passed through, is large, industrial, and dirty—but Kyoto! The little we've seen is enchanting and we are to have almost a week here. A lot of the train ride was most interesting—every inch of the countryside is cultivated, terraced, and neat as a pin—not a scrap of land is wasted.

Saturday we were taken en masse to see the Imperial Palace and the acres of buildings which had been set up for the coronation. It was a ghastly afternoon and the first and last time I'll go with the whole mob! That evening was much better—Miss Douglas, Addy, and I took rickshas to a Japanese tea house. The ride was picturesque, with glimpses from time to time down canals or tiny rivers where people were washing clothes along the banks by the light of the moon—the temperature was thirty-three degrees above zero!

When we left the rickshas we walked through a Japanese garden of rocks and scrub pine between screen houses. A girl in a most colorful kimono greeted us at the door of one. As we took off our shoes and stepped onto the mats of the tiny room we saw just one precious vase of flowers on the floor. There was nothing else in the room except for cushions on which we were invited to sit, cross-legged.

The girl brought in three bronze braziers containing glowing charcoal. She set them on the floor near us and it was amazing how quickly they warmed us and the room. In the center of our triangle she set a large brazier on a lacquer tray or frame.

Next she came in with a tier of trays, each one divided into many compartments and in each was some kind of food to be cooked. I recognized chicken, bean cakes, something which looked like romaine, slices of water radish, bamboo shoots, and many other things I wouldn't pretend to know. As she proceeded to add various bits of food from her many trays, we were delighted to watch her graceful movements —it was a completely artistic piece of work from beginning to end—this preparation of our meal. When it was ready it tasted as perfect as it looked. The Saki which was served hot in thimble-sized cups was an ideal complement to the dish (sukiyaki).

* * * * *

Kyoto, Dec. 25th

Dearest Mother and Phyl:

Sunday morning we all went to Nara, the oldest Japanese city and the first seat of government, so we were told. The famous park there is lovely and filled with deer. We strolled about by ourselves and carefully avoided the temple, except to see it from a distance, as we suspected we were going to have to see many of these later on. We did inspect the huge pagoda there more closely.

On someone's bright inspiration (someday I'll have to discover whose it was), a small group of us left Nara early and on our own hooks started off on a trip. We took trains, a tram, and finally a cable car up a mountain. At about two thousand feet up we started walking up a flagstoned street past small shops and tea houses where we heard no English at all. After passing through this tiny community (Naraken), we followed a path through a tori (gate) into the woods. For about a mile this path was lined on either side by stone lanterns. It finally brought us to a sheltered valley where we saw several buildings. This was Shigisan Yamato, a monastery we'd never heard of and, as far as I'm concerned, it is still not real.

After some wandering about we reached the main part of the monastery where we found one of the monks. With sign language, we made him understand we should like to stay the night. He and another welcomed us most hospitably, bowing and scraping as if we had been invited guests! Before too long we were fortunate in meeting a Japanese pilgrim who spoke some English. He went out of his way to help. When the "monks" found that we had come all the way from America they seemed delighted.

They promptly led us to a lovely building, most restrained in design. This was built around a small court in which was a rock and miniature pine garden. Upstairs was one hall onto which two large rooms opened—one on either side. The whole structure was built of screens or what we would call paper walls.

The larger of the two rooms was practically empty. There was a raised platform or dais at one end on which stood a small cabinet and a beautifully carved cypress stand. On this there was a yellow vase containing branches of red and ivory berries. On the wall at the back was a single large print in black and white of trees and a waterfall. There was nothing else in the room except mats and colored cushions on the floor where we were invited to sit, the monks indicating that this was our home.

We spent some of the late afternoon wandering around the enchanting place marveling at every perfection. Then with our pilgrim friend we drank tea out of beautiful lacquer cups and ate rice cakes.

Next we were offered the hospitality of a Japanese bath. It was one community room (we girls used it first and then the boys). There we found a very deep tub full of extremely hot water into which we climbed (it was only later that we found we shouldn't have done so). Following this we doused each other with buckets of ice cold water. On returning to our lovely room we were given warm, quilted kimonos to put on over our clothes and invited to sit on the cushions. Bronze braziers full of glowing coals were already in place to warm the room.

Three monks then brought in tiers of red and black lacquer trays and put one of each before each of us. Wooden buckets full of hot fluffy rice were passed, our bowls were filled, and we helped ourselves to many kinds of delicacies, placing them on the rice. Chopsticks were our only tools and we did pretty well with them. I have no idea what I ate —maybe snails and puppy dog's tails—but it was all heavenly!

Since this was the night before Christmas Eve, we all must have felt in a similar mood—so far from home. Someone started to sing a Christmas carol—everyone joined in and we went on to another and another. The three precious monks who served us remained kneeling in the center of our group of eight during the entire time!

Addy and I went out for a walk following a trail up the mountain which was arched over by what seemed several hundred toris. When we neared the top we found a pilgrim kneeling at a little shrine and chanting. We stopped some distance from him so as not to disturb him. His chant was a weird one. It was all so strange but so lovely—we could see for some miles in the moonlight—just the tops of other mountains with a heavy mist farther down below them. Directly below us we could see the lights of Shigisan and leading away from those was a double winding trail of lights —the stone lanterns we had seen when coming up.

Later we went down to the village, a colorful enchanting community where everyone seemed to be out on the one street. We tried out our two or three words of Japanese and caused great amusement. The one word I'll always remember is that lovely Sayonara (good evening or good night).

Arriving back at the monastery we found that our kind hosts had spread enough beds for all of us on the floor of the two rooms. These consisted of softly quilted pads, almost like feather beds—we had three apiece. It was lovely to go to sleep watching the frosted wall screens—the moonlight behind them brought out the design of great bells which we hadn't seen in daylight.

Early next morning they held a special prayer service for us in the temple—It was a weird business with much beating of drums and sounding of bells and reading of sacred books. (My sacrilegious mind saw the readers of the books as card sharps shuffling packs of cards between widespread hands!) Our pilgrim friend told us they were asking a blessing on us from their gods and godspeed on our journey. As we stepped out of the temple a gorgeous sunrise greeted us over the same lovely peaks we'd seen by moonlight and the valleys below were still shrouded in mist.

Late Christmas Night

Back at Nara to join the main group we took rickshas to see the Diabutsu (probably the largest Buddha in the world). It was some fifty feet high and stood in a penetratingly cold, damp temple. No wonder these people worship that thing! If I had been brought up in that religion and saw that image I'd be too terrified to do anything but worship him!

Once more Miss Douglass saved us from a large group trip and about six of us went with her after we had returned to Kyoto, on a trip to visit the shops. These were where the best of Japanese Damascene, Cloisonné, and lacquer are made, exhibited, and sold. At each we saw the process of manufacture (in the true sense of the word). In the lacquer factory, for instance, there was a large room with rows of workmen sitting cross-legged on the floor. Each man was working on an individual piece of work. One was rubbing or sanding a delicate piece of wood; another was applying one of many coats of lacquer, etc.

When we reached one man seated before a fairly large piece of furniture we stopped to watch him for some time. It was a sort of secretary he was working on and it looked about finished to us. He was working on the design, which is usually put on before the last, umteenth, coat of clear lacquer is to be applied. It was a lacy, delicate design which was obviously going to cover a large area. On the black background of the previous coat of finish he was laying out tiny specks of gold leaf. These he handled with a finely

59

pointed pair of forceps (such as a scientist back home would use for dissecting an insect). As we watched, fascinated by his every move, he would place an infinitesimal piece, look at it, adjust its position, and then, perhaps, remove it—and start all over again.

In astonishment, I asked the foreman, an English-speaking man who guided us, "How long has that man been working on that piece?"

The reply was, "All his life. His father started it and his son will finish it."

"But—but doesn't one have to see his finished work for his own satisfaction?"

"No, not a real Japanese artisan—he knows his father has done a perfect job. He, for his part, will do a perfect job and he is convinced that he has trained his son to do the same. Therefore he doesn't have to live to see it."

After having seen these lovely things being made, we were led, in each case, into the shop where the finished articles were for sale. We were seated about a table and tea and rice cakes were served. Following this and some polite conversation, one lovely bowl, cup, or other object was brought in and laid on a piece of velvet. We could feast our eyes on it with no distractions. Then another piece was brought in, etc. The only reason I'm not broke right now is that I don't have enough money to buy one exquisite piece in a place like that and all the ordinary things in regular shops now have little attraction.

That was Christmas Eve, and Christmas Day; Today Miss Douglass, Addy, and I spent the afternoon in Yamanaka's art gallery and shop combined. We almost lost our minds over jades, ivories, silks, prints, bronzes, wood carvings, etc. A lovely way to spend Christmas in a foreign land!

* * * * *

The couple sat on, smoking cigarettes and finishing their drinks. For a time neither of them spoke. Then the woman looked at her watch.

"It's well after three—I'm supposed to take a train soon after four."

"Do you have to?"

"No, I guess not, but I did say I'd have dinner with my

60

cousins in Chappaqua. What about you? You've just come back from Chicago and must be anxious to get on home."

"The trains run every hour. I told my wife that I was having lunch with you. I asked her to join us but she just said, 'No, thank you. If you don't show up by Sunday night, though, I'll start worrying about you.' "

"Well, in that case I'll phone M. A. and tell her to expect me when she sees me."

"How about a sandwich? I did ask you for lunch?"

When the woman came back from the phone the waiter brought sandwiches and coffee to the table.

"You heard that Lucille Douglass died some years ago, didn't you?"

"Yes, but just the fact; I don't know anything else about her. What a grand gal she was! And what a difference she made! We would have missed a good deal if it hadn't been for her."

"I kept track of a few people for awhile. In many ways I'd like to go to the 25th reunion in San Francisco next month."

"I may go. I told Connie Raises over the phone a few days ago that I might—but I don't think I'd remember anyone except you and Fritz, and if you and he can't be there—."

"Speaking of keeping in touch—do you hear from the Osakis?"

"No, I'm afraid I've lost that contact too. I have, of course, read about him in *Time,* and the last news was that Yukio was still alive. He must be well past ninety. You knew, didn't you, that Madame Osaki died—before the war, I believe."

* * * * *

Miyako Hotel Kyoto
December 27, 1928

Dearest family:

Just returned from the Nishi-Hongkwangi Temple where we saw some very rare and lovely paintings. The screens had been brought from Hideoshi's Palace. Most of them were done in gold. It is wonderful to be seeing and doing all this with good friends who see and feel as I do. Miss Douglass continues to be a grand advisor in all sorts of ways. Addy and Fritz are both darlings—how lucky I am!

61

The Kanaya Hotel
Nikko, Japan
Dec. 30, 1928

Phyl, dear:

It was a ten-hour train ride up here in second-class cars. There were just long wooden seats running the length of the car—not exactly comfortable! To get to the diner we had to stagger through miles of third-class Japanese passengers who were jammed-in a lot worse than we were.

The countryside was lovely and we had a pretty good view of Fujisan (Fujiyama) although the tip of the mountain was covered with clouds.

We are now split into two divisions. The other group leaves Japan in a day or two. They will have only a brief stop in China and then go to Java. Our group will have longer here and in China.

Yesterday we had a brief time in Tokyo—a most modern city which has been surprisingly built up since the earthquake. Addy and I had tea in Frank Lloyd Wright's Imperial Hotel which became so famous for withstanding the quake.

This place is the Lake Placid of Japan. It is lovely with pine woods and lots of clean white snow, as it is high in the mountains. Wish we could stay over New Year's.

Lord knows what is going to happen—today I am head-over-heels in love with Addy! (This is not for publication.)

Later

There was a full moon and Addy and I went down into the village, snooping about the shops, looking at old silks, ivories, and gorgeous brocades.

Early next morning we took a car up into the mountains to Lake Chusengi. There we left the car and walked back along the side of a stream. At one point there was a beautiful waterfall over a hundred feet high.

After getting back to the hotel we walked to see a number of the shrines and small temples. The settings in the hills among magnificent Cryptomeria trees were lovely. In one of the temples we saw the original monkeys—Hear no evil, See no evil, and Speak no evil.

Back in Tokyo a few of us shared a bottle of champagne.

We were glad of a couple of days' rest and barely kept awake to see the New Year in.

Kamakura Kaihin Hotel
Kamakura, Japan
Jan. 6, 1929

Dearest family:

On the third we came down here to Kamakura. A very short time after our arrival I was told that there was some-one to see me. I went out to the front drive and there was Shinaye Osaki on horseback! I'd written her from Tokyo and she had ridden over from Zushi (the next stop south of Kamakura) where she and her family now live. She was much the same as when we'd seen her last at camp and asked all about you, Phyl, as well as others she had known at camp. She then invited me to tea the next day and asked me to bring six or seven of my closest friends with me.

Jane George, Howard Marshall, Ayres Compton, Ruth Henderson, Eddie Dorland, and, of course, Fritz and Addy took the train with me, and in a short time we reached the doll-like village of Zushi. Shinaye had two cars awaiting us which drove us some little distance beyond the village to the bottom of a hill. There an old man, the gardener, I guess, met us and proceeded to lead us up a long flight of winding steps to the house. It was perched right on the top of the hill. One side of this fell away steeply to the sea and from practically every window one had a lovely view of the bay, the tiny village, or the terraced landscape on either side.

We were greeted most cordially by Shinaye and her mother. The latter (who is half English) is like a Dresden doll—tiny, with a lovely face and one of the sweetest expressions I've ever seen. We were introduced to Shinaye's sister and a number of Japanese guests. All seemed very nice but quite bashful. However, it didn't take too long to get acquainted; most of them spoke a fair amount of English but none of them so well as Madame Osaki and Shinaye, who, as you know, went to Wellesley as well as to camp for some years.

The house itself was most attractive, with lovely things in it. It was a blend of East and West—the beautiful simplicity of Japanese design plus the comfort of occidental furniture. There was American music and we all danced a bit before sliding doors to the dining room were opened. There was a table laden with quantities of American food—even to homemade apple pie!

Shinaye's father joined us for awhile—what a remarkable man he is! He's tiny in stature but very distinguished looking, with a most magnetic personality. He is very deaf and uses a long wooden ear trumpet. Of course you know he is one of the biggest men in Japan, having been responsible for the modernization of Tokyo as well as being a member of the Japanese Diet for forty-two consecutive years.

Saturday night there was to be a dance at our hotel, so I invited Shinaye and a cousin who was visiting her to join us for dinner and the party. Everyone seemed to have a good time. Madame Osaki came after dinner to watch the dancing. I suspected she was worried about the girls being with a bunch of foreigners. Later, I felt sure that she just wanted to be in on it herself. She was surrounded all evening by American boys and girls and danced several times! She is completely charming.

When the party was over, Addy and I drove the three of them back to their home. On the way, in a narrow village street we saw three Japanese firemen dressed in the most picturesque uniforms. I guess they were returning from a fire. In any case they were obviously "under the influence." Madame Osaki was enchanted by them and enchanting in her amusement over them. I wish I could describe how I felt—I was in a Japanese fairyland and nothing was real.

I turned to Shinaye and said, "All I can think of is a book of Japanese fairy tales I loved as a child." I added, "Was it Lafcadio Hearn?"

Shinaye told me that her mother had translated that and many other books into English. We left the three with the gardener who came foreward with a lantern and led them safely up the winding path between the rows of stone lanterns.

Sunday morning a few of us met Shinaye on the train for Tokyo. She had planned with her instructor for us to attend her class in Tea Ceremony. This particular one was to be in the nature of a "graduation."

Wish I could describe this ceremony. All of it was done to the accompaniment of a strange weird music played on a stringed instrument such as I'd never seen before. Each student, in turn, went through the procedure of preparing the tea, greeting his or her guests, offering the cup, and drinking the brew. It was like nothing I'd ever imagined. Every move was completely graceful and each had a real meaning. To these people this essence of hospitality is a sign of true civilization. After they have mastered the mechanics of it they study the philosophy behind it. It is something entirely beyond our Western comprehension. Even after seeing it I don't pretend to understand it, but we were all terribly impressed by the grace, beauty, and dignity of it all.

I couldn't understand how, after sitting cross-legged on the floor for over two hours without moving or speaking, we could rise to our feet without feeling stiff or tired at all! I, for one, felt entirely relaxed and refreshed!

Sunday night Shinaye telephoned to tell us how much she had enjoyed it all and to say that her mother had a special message for us—she invited us back in cherry blossom time! Surely it is we who are eternally indebted to the Osakis for making our stay in Japan so very special. (Just as Washington, D.C. is indebted to Yukyo who brought the cherry trees there.)

* * * * *

People had started coming into the Pierre for cocktails and the room was soon crowded. The waiter approached the corner table and suggested mildly that he might remove the coffee cups and half-eaten sandwiches. He took this opportunity to remove the lunch cloth and replace it with cocktail mats. The engrossed couple paid little attention to him or anything around them and continued talking.

"I wish I could have seen Fritz in Washington when I was there to see father. I just missed him by a few hours. You've seen him, haven't you?"

"Yes, from time to time. Did you know that he has done very well in the State Department?"

"Friends in Wisconsin have sent me occasional clippings about him, so actually I know a bit more about him than I do about anyone else in our entire 'gang' until today. He was very nice to me in England when I went over to meet my sister's fiance. A crazy trip, I'll tell you about it someday."

"I've never gotten back, but I gather you have more than once?"

"Yes, several times—I've been very fortunate—but only to Europe, never to China or the Orient. And now China is out of the question for anyone."

"So many Americans have been to Japan now, since the war. I wonder if it has changed much. I hope my children will be able to see something of the world before they settle down."

"It seems to me that one of the encouraging things about the world today is the fact that so many people have been about more. I know that having been to Japan made a difference to me while Bill was on active duty in the Pacific. Even though he died as a result of it I could still think of them as human beings."

"How lucky we were to have had that trip—just before the Depression and while most of the world was at peace."

"No one can take it away from us—but there were War Lords in China. Remember we couldn't get to Peking. I wonder if that was real or if it was an excuse."

"I don't think it was an excuse. Don't you remember the concrete machine-gun nests in Canton and the gunboat and the platoon of soldiers?"

* * * * *

Aboard S.S. President Jefferson
January 14, 1929

Mother darling:

This ship is almost a replica of the Wilson.

In a way I was glad to leave Japan while I was so very keen about it. We didn't try to do too much and I think the impressions we did receive will stay with us longer.

Friday the eleventh we landed in Shanghai after a most picturesque sail through the Inland Sea. We docked across and somewhat upriver from Shanghai proper and took tenders to and from the city.

The visit was rather unsatisfactory as we only had two days there and the cruise people had arranged for receptions, speeches, etc. Addy and I managed to break away a few times and wandered about the streets and had a few hours to shop along the Bund. We did hate to leave so soon. China is much as one might expect it to be—dirty, crowded, smelly, but colorful and fascinating. The people are so cheerful and friendly—even when trying their best to cheat you! You can't help loving them!

The Victoria Hotel
Shameen, Canton, China
January 16, 1929

Phyl, dear:

Now we are really in China. We came into Hong Kong harbor at night. I can well believe it is the most beautiful harbor in the world, except maybe San Francisco.

Coming into the harbor was like drifting into a perfect fairyland of lights. The cruisers and battleships and all the other craft down to the smallest junks, were lighted, duplicated by their reflections in the water. In the background the city lights rose right up the hillside so that one couldn't tell the lights on top from the stars.

We took a tender in the morning to Hong Kong and spent the day wandering about the shops and flower markets —such a riot of color!

After dinner we boarded a British river steamer and came up here to Canton on an overnight trip. Of course it is much warmer here—quite springlike and we are already using mosquito nettings.

Aboard S.S. President Hayes
January 28, 1929

Mother darling:

I have neglected writing for some time but since I'm sure my letters arrive in bunches some weeks later, I guess it doesn't really matter. Do you know I've only had one letter from home since San Francisco?!

I think I last wrote just after we had reached Canton. On the whole it was a relaxed, lazy time on the Island of Shameen, the foreign settlement there. . . .

One day we rode into the country on ridiculous little Chinese horses which were horrible but it was fun and the day was lovely. The countryside was interesting but far from beautiful, much of it being very barren, with nothing growing except gravestones.

We have made several trips across the river into the native city. Incidentally, the street corners in the foreign settlement all have concrete machine-gun nests and there is barbed wire at the bridges and along the shore of the island.

The city, proper, of Canton is fascinating if filthy. There are whole streets of silk shops, streets where nothing but ivory is sold—others of jade, amber, etc. Most shops were tiny cubbyholes open to the street, but the wares were lovely. I bought a length of lovely raw silk, and a tailor who came to the hotel made me an evening dress in two days!

Last Monday we went on a trip to the back country. We took a train first, for two hours, and then at some godforsaken little village boarded two flower boats, or junks. These were towed by a Chinese gunboat up the Pearl River into fairly hilly and quite pretty country. We anchored for the night. We were supposed to have arrived earlier and gone on up to a monastery. As it was, we spent the night on the junks. What a night!

We did have some pillows and blankets but no beds. All the furniture consisted of carved teakwood tables and chairs, and HARD! I slept (?) on three chairs pulled together.

In the middle of the night a boat passed, causing some good-sized waves. Since our two junks were lashed together, the waves banged them against each other and caused quite a commotion. One of the older women immediately thought it was bandits boarding us and started quite a lot of excitement among those who were inclined to be hysterical.

In the morning we were glad to leave our hard beds. When we went ashore we were met by a bodyguard of ten soldiers! They were to conduct us to the monastery. Some of us walked but a good many were carried in sedan chairs along the most circuitous path (they called it a road) that I have ever seen. They tell us that all the roads have to wind about in that way because there are so many graves all over the

68

countryside and these can't ever be disturbed!

The monastery was a stone structure, cold, dark, and dismal. The view from up there was nice and the people very cordial. They gave us plenty of food but it wasn't very good!

On the way down, Addy and I left ahead of the rest and followed a nice mountain stream, not bothering to stay on the trail. Later, when the rest caught up with us, still marching behind their guards, we were told that no one was supposed to have gone alone—too dangerous! We will have to confess to our grandchildren in future years that we never had a glimpse of a bandit!

The afternoon trip down-river on our flower boats went quickly. Getting aboard the little train, Addy and I bribed the engineer to let us ride in the engine cab with him. It turned out to be the roughest ride we ever had—and the dirtiest! A further drawback was the fact that the engineer, like all Oriental drivers of any kind of vehicle, insisted on blowing the whistle and ringing the bell continuously. When we reached Canton we were not only black with soot but deaf as well!

Our last day and night in China was spent in Kowloon across the bay from Hong Kong.

The Hayes is not nearly so nice as the Wilson but it has a pleasant afterdeck for tea dancing. It is hot and we are all in white—very festive.

We're headed for the Philippines—if I don't get some mail in Singapore I think I'll stop writing letters! Even so, I love you, am completely happy, and wouldn't change places with anyone in the world!

* * * * *

"Would you like another drink? I would. Waiter! I suppose I do more of this than I should, but this *is* an occasion."

"After my husband died I drank a lot more than was good for me. I'm better now in many ways. Why not have another? Remember Rangoon? What was the expression?—Have another peg, Joe? What was the name of that British-India ship?"

"The S.S. Ekma. But before that—that trip up the Malay

peninsula was enough to drive anyone to drink!—the tropics generally!"

"Maybe that accounted in part for the revolution we had in Bangkok. I must say I don't remember much of what it was all about, now."

"Young as we were, I think we were pretty smart in steering clear of the wrangling, don't you?"

"S. S. Ekma—how do you remember? I can recall that we had a lot of peaceful days on her. I've always been sorry we didn't get to Angkor or Mandalay, but I guess that long rest from sightseeing was a real break for us, certainly for me."

"And for me, too. That was really the only time on the entire trip that so few of us congenial people could be ourselves for any extended period of time. We can thank Connie Raises for that."

"I suspect that he enjoyed that relaxing time, too."

* * * * *

Singapore
February 4, 1929

Mother darling:

We just arrived a few minutes ago. Thank you for your birthday cable as well as the one you sent to Manila. How you manage to get so much news into so few words is a miracle! I must admit it takes me some time to decipher them! I also got two letters from you and Phyl. They were written a long time ago and make you seem very far away. . . .

Our stay in Manila was very short but it was pleasant to set foot on American soil. Thanks to Miss Douglass we had a card to the Army and Navy club and pool. We did have a couple of interesting drives around the city and then out into the country where we saw masses of little thatched houses built on stilts.

Later

After traipsing about this city for a few hours in the heat and the rain we were so exhausted that I quite hated the place. However, it didn't take too long to discover that the thing to do here, two degrees off the equator, is to sleep from

70

eleven AM to about four in the afternoon. As a matter of fact, I slept until five today. Then Addy and I, all dressed up in white, went tea dancing at the famous Raffles Hotel. Later we had a lovely cool drive around the city. The top of the car was down and we had a nice Sikh chauffeur.

Singapore is far different from my preconceived ideas of it. It has lots of space, quite beautiful architecture, and wide streets. It wasn't nearly so crowded as I expected. The people one does see, though, are a strange lot of every size, shape, and color imaginable. The atmosphere is British, as it was in Hong Kong. I guess my impression of lack of crowds here is because we have so recently come from China.

Phya Tai Palace
Bangkok, Siam
February 10

Dearest Mother and Phyl:

That was some trip up here from Singapore! The first night and day we were in third-class Malay cars. That means glorified boxcars. With straight up-and-down wooden benches—too short to lie down on and too close together to allow one to stretch out on the floor. Addy and I spent the better part of the night sitting on the back platform of the train—and I don't mean observation platform!

The second night we had second-class coaches to ride in. These had stretcher-like wooden shelves that let down from the side walls of the cars—infinitely better! The toilets (incidentally, one in each car for men and women alike) were closed-off tiny cubicles with a hole in the floor. There was a pipe running down one wall, with occasional drops coming from it.

I recall that at one point during the night I woke up to see the girl in the upper across from me sitting bolt upright with a look of terror on her face. She said nothing but she pointed her finger at the lower bunk behind me. I crawled out, half asleep, to see Norma Felder curled up sound asleep on her hard bed. Behind her bent knees the cotton blanket was merrily burning—a bright little fire! I grabbed the girl and shoved her to the floor, much to her disgust. Then others who awoke and I beat out the flames in the blanket and thin mattress beneath.

After the excitement was all over and we settled down, I had a lot of thoughts. The engine burned wood; large sparks and chunks of coals flew from the stack and scattered about. I could still see many flying past the car window. Because it was really hot, even at night, all our windows were open. If someone hadn't awakened, there could have been a real fire which could have spread to all the wooden cars in the rear. We were racing through uninhabited jungle and what might have happened gave me the heebie-jeebies for some nights to come!

Anyway, we got here safely and Siam is fascinating! The people are most attractive and so colorful! Their architecture is beautiful, if a bit ornate. However, it is not garish as are so many of the Buddhist structures we have seen up until now. The use of color is lovely, predominantly russet and green.

This hotel was formerly the Royal Palace. The rooms are spacious, the gardens are beautiful and well kept, and the food, mostly French in character, is delicious.

It's no wonder this country has kept her independence while so many around her are under foreign control. These people are up-and-coming and very modern in their attitude. There is a sense of contentment here which I've felt in few other places we've visited. There is so much to see that we are picking and choosing from the terrific program which has been laid out for us. We aren't going to Angkor—Miss Douglass is taking a few people with her but it is too expensive for me to manage—I'll probably regret not going, some day. I'm sure Addy isn't taking the trip because I am not —and that is bad—I can't persuade him otherwise.

There have been a lot of internal upsets within the cruise group. Some of us are very fed up with the dissensions, petty gossip, etc. About sixteen of us are leaving here ahead of the rest of them.

Nanking Hotel
Penang, Malaya
February 5, 1929

Mother darling:

Well, we got away from the large gang. Connie Raises, an assistant manager of the cruise, is taking care of the mechanical part of our travel, although how he manages without money we don't know! Probably that is why we are in this horrible hotel which looks so grand in the picture. We're housed in the basement, with an open sewer running down the hall!

To go back a minute—I did love Bangkok. We went to see the Grand Palace and the imperial temple. We also took a day's launch trip along the innumerable rivers and canals. Thousands of people live out their whole lives on the water—a very interesting if odoriferous trip.

The trip down here was luxurious—first class! However, because of a burned bridge on the line, we were held up for eight hours in the steaming jungle! We sail for Burma tomorrow.

* * * * *

Aboard S. S. Ekma
British India Line
Rangoon, Burma
February 22, 1929

Mother darling:

We are at anchor in the bay at the south end of the Irriwaddy River. These last peaceful days have been heavenly. We've had a few classes and I've written an art paper and have read up fairly thoroughly on Burma and India.

Some days we go over to Rangoon and visit the fascinating markets. Today we went up the Shwe Dagon Pagoda. It is a fabulous structure with a bell-shaped dome covered with gold. It is really impossible to describe. As it is a shrine we had to remove our shoes and stockings before we were allowed to climb the scores of steps. Someone tipped us off ahead of time and we escaped picking up too much dirt and germs by plastering the soles of our feet with adhesive tape! Fortunately for us it was some kind of fete day so there were hordes of people going up and down—a most picturesque sight. Both men and women wore gorgeous silks in brilliant colors. The monks here wear robes that are a lovely burnt-orange color. It was quite a sight as the people bowed and kneeled at the shrine, chanting and going through a complicated ritual.

When we don't go over to Rangoon we hang over the rail and bargain with the natives in their little boats full of colorful products. Ayres Compton, Fritz, Addy, and I have a running bridge tournament and Addy is teaching me chess. It's heaven to have these relaxing days!

* * * * *

The Grand Hotel Ltd.
Chowringhee Road
Calcutta, India
February 27, 1929

Mother darling:

Lots of mail was forwarded here today and it was so good to get your letters plus many Christmas cards.

We are now getting ready for our seven-day train ride across India. It will take us to Lucknow, Benares, Delhi, Agra, Bombay, and Madras—some program!

Our drive around Calcutta (presumably the largest city in the world, though no one can prove it) was a memorable one. The contrasts between wealth and poverty were colossal. The dirt and smells indescribable—worse than what we experienced in China. Also, the people here are glum and unresponsive—one never sees a smile.

(The following excerpts were written in snatches crossing India but not mailed till Bombay.)

Our stop in Lucknow was brief but exceptional in that we had a chance to take baths in the large station.

Benares was unforgettable. The trip to the Ganges and a good part of the day there was something! Because the river is considered holy, it was (and I guess always is) filled with people who bathe their faces, hands, arms, as well as hair, while standing in the filthy water. They also drank it and filled jars with it to take home in order to bless those who couldn't come there.

Along the shore we saw two burning ghats. These were simply bonfires on which the people burned their dead—the bodies in many cases having been carried by hand from miles away. For those whose relatives or friends had little or no money for enough—or any—firewood, the bodies were partly burned. The remains, in any case, were simply thrown into the filthy but holy river!

The balance of the time in Benares we visited many shops full of gold and silver brocades, silks, Kashmir weaves, ivories, jade, and precious jewels. The contrast between these and the homeless, starving, and dying people in the street gutters and in doorways was, as in Calcutta, incredible.

We are traveling in second-class Indian railway cars and sometimes busses. The cars are compartmented—five people to a compartment. We each have one towel and one so-called cotton blanket—to last us, unwashed, for seven days till Bombay! The cars do not communicate with one another so it is necessary to get off at some stop somewhere near meal- or bedtime and dash to the diner—or back to one's own car, and hope that the next stop won't be too many hours away. We are dirty and hot by day, sightseeing, and dirty and cold by night—with the train racketing over an extremely rough roadbed.

* * * * *

Later. Don't
know the day or date.

I can see now that this screed won't be mailed until we reach Bombay. The train stopped at Alahabad, also at a few other places, long enough for us to get ourselves sorted out and into our own cars periodically.

* * * * *

The dinner crowd had filled the restaurant and many people had finished eating and were leaving for the theater and other places. The waiter (a new one by this time) approached the table with a menu in his hand. The man and woman looked at each other and decided without speaking that they needed some air before eating.

As they turned down Fifth Avenue the evening was still

hot and sticky after the air-conditioning of the Pierre, but neither of them paid much attention to it. Arm-in-arm they strolled, oblivious of the passersby.

"Do you realize that we've seen most of the important places of the world together—except for New York?"

The man held out his hand to the woman. They crossed Fifth Avenue without a word and climbed into a horse-drawn carriage in front of the Plaza. The old driver slapped his horse with the reins and started for Central Park.

"India was so horrible in so many ways, wasn't it? But I wouldn't have missed it for anything—especially Delhi and Agra—"

"That train—and the dirt—remember the cigarettes that cost so much?"

"But, no matter what, the moon was always in the right place at the right time."

* * * * *

Bombay

To continue—dear family—

When we reached Delhi we were left on our own until noon. Addy and I took a little jogging cart in which we rode with our backs to the driver and visited many fascinating shops.

After luncheon we were driven to see the mosques, etc. The Delhi Fort which was so famous in the Sepoy Mutiny was by far the most interesting place we saw. Within the Fort are the lovely palaces of several of the great Shahs. That of Shah Jehan was the most beautiful of all, being built of marble inlaid with agate, carnelian, turquoise, and goldstone. We were told that emeralds and other precious stones had at one time been in the designs but had long since been removed.

The Pearl Mosque, also within the Fort, is perfectly exquisite in its simplicity of line, whiteness of marble, and charm of design. Oh, this Mohammedan architecture! Nothing I've seen in Japan, China, Siam, or Burma can compare with it!

Later we went out to see one of the huge minarets. It is about two hundred and fifty feet high. We went up to the top and got an excellent view of the desolate countryside. It overlooked one of the former sites of Delhi which is now nothing but ruins.

Addy and I did get away from the mob for an hour or so. We drove to the Maiden's Hotel, looking very grimy (at least I did), and boldly walked into the lounge to order a drink. We were appalled when people started coming in in full evening dress! However, we didn't back out! I'll never forget the snooty look on the face of the waiter who brought us our drinks. When we asked for cigarettes he produced a cylindrical can of 50 Abdullahs. It cost us something like five dollars! Since then we smoke a few puffs at a time, stub them out, and then relight them at a later time!

Back on the train, we reached Agra about four in the morning. I guess we were supposed to sleep until daylight but the Frasers, Ayres, Addy, and I got up and took the only available taxi out to the Taj Mahal.

The moon, fortunately, was on the wane and still in the sky at our backs at that hour as we approached the big gates. Richard Halliburton, to the contrary notwithstanding, when we knocked on the gates an old Hindu opened a small door and let us in. The others went on ahead and Addy and I had the whole thing to ourselves! Our first view was just two black rows—avenues of cedars on either side—framing the Taj which was absolutely white in the moonlight. It was dream stuff—reflected in the series of pools before it.

As we slowly walked toward the Taj the black Arabic characters and the mosaics, instead of looking like the inlaid work it was, made the white marble background appear as if it were carved in an intricate, lacy pattern. Then we went into the building and another old man guided us around. We didn't stay there long but walked out into the gardens through another long avenue of trees; then looked back at the Taj from another angle. From there we could see just a section of the face of the structure, framed by the black foliage. It was far too like a dream to describe in words. All my fears about having the Taj Mahal spoiled for me by too enthusiastic descriptions beforehand were forgotten.

After breakfast we were taken across the river to see Shah Jehan's Palaces and the Jasmine Tower from which the Shah looked toward the Taj in the days of his imprisonment.

Later in the day we went back to see it in daylight—nothing could have been as lovely as our first sight, but we were glad we went back—the grace of line and the colors of the mosaics were beyond description. How lucky we are!

Hotel Connemara
Madras, India
March 7, 1929

Dearest Mother:

Our stopover in Bombay was all too short a time in which to get rested up before getting on a train again. It was wonderful to have a real bath, though!

We went out to see the Towers of Silence where the Parsees bring their dead and lay them out on grids for the buzzards. All flesh is picked from the bones in no time at all and the skeletons fall into a common grave below. It sounds rather grisly but I think there is much to be said for the custom. Certainly it is better than the burning ghats and it sounds better to me than mouldering in a grave.

Addy bought me a lovely sandal- and teakwood jewel box which is inlaid with ivory, silver, and turquoise. We are to be here only a few hours—the temples are terrible.

Grand Oriental Hotel
Colombo, Ceylon

Dearest Family:

Just had to write a note on this paper with an elephant on it.

The rest of the southern India trip was interesting but hot and dirty.

About four yesterday we got on a ferry at a point opposite northern Ceylon. The trip across the Paulk Straits was really rough and many were seasick who hadn't been previously. Think they were laid low by the smell of decayed fish and filthy natives more than by the choppy waves. Addy and I stayed up in the bow and got well drenched by the spray —it was lovely to be on the water again.

This country is gorgeous—everything wet and lush
—heavenly after hot, dry India.

S.S. City of Baroda
J.R.E. Hall Line
March 17, 1929

Mother dear:

We've been on the Baroda a week now, but you'll probably
get this about the same time as my note mailed in Ceylon. A
group of us took a car and drove over eighty miles of the Island. We were dying to make the trip to Kandy but there
just wasn't time. Every bit of the drive was lovely—wet,
jade-green vegetation, millions of palm trees, acres of cin-
namon and tea plantations, etc. The people there are really
beautiful—clean, healthy, and happylooking in brilliantly
colored clothes. It think it quite likely that this is the original paradise they claim for it.

* * * * *

The carriage had stopped. They were back in front of the
Plaza once more. The driver had turned in his high seat and
was looking down at them but he didn't say a word.

The man and the woman started in surprise to find themselves in New York in 1954 instead of on the Island of
Ceylon in 1929. The sky was almost dark and the city lights
had come on. The man paid the driver and then handed the
woman down from the carriage.

Arm-in-arm they continued down Fifth Avenue on the
west side of the street. Looking about him in the warm, soft
evening, the man said,

"Who was the man you threw me over for?"

"After twenty-five years it doesn't make much difference,
does it? As a matter of fact you may know him, he teaches at
your university. He threw *me* over a year later."

"Why, the so-and-so! Do you mind if I tell my wife? She'd
get a kick out of it. She never did think much of him."

"He was fascinating to me in those days, but I must say he
didn't hurt me as much as I hurt myself when I turned you
down."

"I never suspected that. Later on I couldn't blame you too

79

much. I realized then what a child I had been and how mixed up I was. Kids these days seem more grown-up. I hope they are."

"The ones I've encountered certainly are—and why shouldn't they be? World War II and Korea made them grow up in a hurry. And with the threat of more war—no wonder they are marrying earlier and having more children. They don't have the time and leisure we had."

"We even had the choice of taking a pokey little ship for seven days in the Mediterranean instead of forty-eight hours from Egypt to Athens."

"Cairo and those lovely mosques! We were rather rushed on the trip up and down the Nile, though. Some of that is pretty much of a blur to me. Remember my twenty-first birthday in Cairo? I didn't think I was so young then, but—"

At that point the couple was standing in front of St. Thomas's Church. The man held out his hand and led the woman up two or three steps where they both sat down and kept on talking while the evening crowd walked by them.

* * * * *

Aboard S.S. Baroda
Later

Dearest Family:

This ship is quite nice, with a canvas swimming pool on deck which has been a godsend on this Arabian sea. Our cabins are pretty stuffy, so that quite a few of us have been sleeping out on deck. It didn't take long to find out that the decks are swabbed down very early in the morning, so there is a race to put one's blanket down on one of the hatch covers. It's all very sociable. I wonder what the turbaned black steward thinks of us all as he stares holes through us to awaken us in the morning.

Classes have started again and I'm taking one in Geography from Dr. H., a Princeton professor, and also a course in Social Anthropology.

We get in lots of swimming which is especially delightful at night as the water is full of phosphorus and it's almost

80

like diving and splashing in fire. When we emerge we drip sparks!

National Hotel
Cairo, March 24, 1929

Dearest Family:

As we got farther north the weather cooled and it seemed good to get out of the tropics. Since the Suez Canal is all on one level it wasn't particularly interesting to go through —nothing like Panama. We disembarked at Fort Said—the less said about that town the better! Suffice it to say that the boys wouldn't let us finish unpacking our trunks which awaited us there—they didn't feel safe on the streets unless accompanied by a female!

This morning a few of us went out with Miss Douglass to "old Cairo" where we saw the very interesting Coptic churches. The first one we saw is said to be the oldest Christian church in existence. It is built over a crypt in which the Holy Family took refuge on their flight into Egypt. It is quite beautiful. The walls are inlaid with ivory, ebony, and cypress. About the nave stand twelve pillars representing the disciples. All of these are of marble except for one of granite which has no capital—for Judas.

In the afternoon we visited the Citadel. This, built by Saladin, is a very imposing sight, standing far above the city. The Mohammed Ali Mosque, presumably all of alabaster, is within the fortress and is really exquisite. The Mohammed Hassein Mosque is the one built of stones taken from the Pyramids, and although not so beautiful as the Ali, was most engrossing and impressive. The archways, one hundred and fifty feet in height, were amazingly graceful.

Our guide was a rare individual and most interesting. He was very frank about what he felt was fact and what fiction. He seemed genuinely anxious to have us learn all about the places we saw. He demanded our attention and stopped more than once to deliver a sermon. One went something like this:

"I am an Arab and Mohammedan. You are American and Christian. But you are my sisters and brothers. It is only what I am at heart which counts—not what I believe or whom I worship. That is what Mohammet taught, that is what Christ taught—and that is what Buddha taught."

Later on he gave us a lecture about obeying our mother. (He was quite convinced that we were all Miss Douglass's children!) We didn't dare express an opinion which differed from hers!

Fairly late that evening a few of us dressed in old clothes and went out to see the pyramids. The moon was full and the night beautiful. We rode camels about and had a very nice first impression of pyramids, mastabas, and the Sphinx.

After visits to bazaars, etc., later on we went to the pyramids by daylight—quite disillusioning. Imagine going to see one of the wonders of the world by streetcar! However, it was interesting to see some of the excavating. The Sphinx is almost all uncovered. We also learned a bit from an Egyptologist; for instance, the measurements of the vast structures all seem to be in inches, feet, and yards; the English system, and yet they were built four thousand years ago!

This time we rode little donkeys and also climbed Cheops. Our one claim to fame in the future may be that we were among the few to do so without carving our initials at the top!

We almost wore ourselves out in the Egyptian Museum. The Tutankhamen rooms were especially worth any amount of time and effort.

(Description of the sarcophagi, jewels, gold, etc., seen there has been left out as these days most people have seen descriptions and colored illustrations of such many times. 1954)

Luxor Winter Palace
Easter Sunday

Dearest Mother:

We just had quite a day in the Valleys of the Kings and Queens. Hot, dry, and dusty. One can pick up a brick and see R. on it for Rameses—how many thousands of years ago?

This afternoon we spent in the ruins of Luxor and Karnak—enormous structures—one can't help being impressed by the immensity of the job of building them, as with the pyramids, but also there is much that is truly artistic as well as mammoth.

Dearest Dallases:

Despite the tiring trip both up and down the Nile, about which I wrote mother, it was something not to be missed.

The trip from Cairo to Kantara, where we crossed to Suez, took three hours. From there another train took us across the desert that is the Sinai. We are again a fairly small group on this jaunt, as many of the others elected to go by ship from Alexandria directly to Athens. They will have longer than we in Greece but we shall see more of the eastern Mediterranean.

The desert train ride might have been dull except for the passport inspector who was a British army officer who was in our compartment. He had fought over this country with General Allenby and had been there also when that railroad was being built to Jerusalem. Again we were lucky to get a different slant on what we were seeing.

Palestine, after the desert, was a most pleasant surprise. It is quite hilly and consequently attractive country. The first day there we walked all around the old walls, getting a comprehensive idea of both the city and the surrounding countryside. At the area where the Temple of the Rock rests over the ancient foundation of Solomon's Temple and where one of the old Crusaders' churches (now a mosque) remains, we were forced to leave the wall. This led us to the Garden of Gethsemane, at the foot of the Mount of Olives.

The garden still contains some of the lovely old olive trees said to date from the time of Christ. Unfortunately the whole place is pretty much spoiled now by the presence of a brand new pink brick Catholic chapel. To make room for this ugly building much of the once beautiful garden with most of its trees was destroyed!

Much of the old city of Jerusalem is charming with its cobbled streets with many steps and graceful archways. The shrine where Mary is supposed to be buried and the Church of the Holy Sepulchre are horrors!

When we got to Bethlehem things were worse. The less said about the place where Jesus was born, the better! What

83

so-called Christians are capable of doing is beyond description! At this point I am tempted to become Mohammedan. Their mosques express such simplicity, good taste, and are so beautiful! These Christian shrines are atrocious. Each sect has seemed to try to outdo the next in draping cheap, gaudy lamps, ribbons, medals, etc., all over the original stable. No one is apparently responsible for keeping the place decently clean or in repair. I'm sorry I ever saw it. The only feature in keeping with my idea of what is suitable is the fact that they have kept the low door to the stable—one has to stoop, almost kneel to enter.

* * * * *

(Still on the steps of St. Thomas)

"Mother is still very spry, she is talking of taking a Mediterranean cruise and wants me to go with her. It sounds wonderful. There are several places I'd like to go back to. I certainly didn't see much of Greece, did I? One thing I've never forgotten was how good you were to me when I was laid up—and all the rest of the time, too. Did I ever thank you?"

"How worried I was about you! It's a wonder how any of us survived the last hectic month or two. I did want to stay on and see England with you and your mother—but?"

"With all the time in the world, I didn't. We only spent three days in London before I sailed for home. I'd had it —travel sick—lovesick. I'm sorry that mother was so disappointed. She wanted to show me Europe. I'm more than fortunate to have been able to get back later, due to the fact that my sister lives in England."

"As I look back, it wouldn't have done me any good to have stayed over longer. I was very travel-weary, too."

"In your case it was especially bad that we sailed west instead of east. Did I ever tell you what Holling said to me weeks before we started the trip?"

"That I don't remember. Was he the chap on the only university cruise before ours?"

"Yes, and one of the first questions he asked me was, 'Which way are you going?' When I said to the Far East first, he asked me if I'd ever been to Europe. I told him I had never been anywhere as yet. Then he said, 'That's too bad.

84

Europe after the Orient is like potatoes after cake!' And it was, wasn't it?"

"Maybe so, but we all had more than anyone else I know. I have no complaints on that score."

"And I have none on any score, unless they are complaints about myself. There were certainly a lot of grand people on that trip, and I remember only a very few and have kept in touch with none. Good Lord, I don't think I half appreciated you!"

"If and when you go to the reunion at San Francisco you might be able to catch up a bit with some of them."

"I doubt it. I don't think I'll go—after today. Do you know I never went back to the Louvre after you and I were there?"

* * * * *

Lloyd Tristino Line
Piroscafo Graz
April 7, 1929

Mother darling:

The Graz is nothing to brag about. She's an old Austrian ship, built long before the war and turned over to the Italians in the post-war settlement. She has a marked list to starboard and my roommates (three of them) and I have a cabin in the extreme stern out over the propeller. I don't know whether we are second or third class, but we took it to avoid an argument. Anyway, to get to the first-class dining room and lounge we have a choice of going through a section where they've quartered a bunch of mules or else go topside at the stern and work our way through masses of deck passengers and their goats who are camped out there for the whole seven- or eight-day trip. When we do eventually get to first class, the food is delicious.

Yesterday we stopped at Beirut for a few hours and had a lovely drive up in the Lebanon hills. From the top we looked back over terrace after terrace of olive groves and could see the city stretched out along the shore of the blue, blue sea.

Later

This is a wonderful old bucket, in spite of our accommoda-

85

can well believe it. She is so unseaworthy that she rolls far over with the slightest wave. Going across a swell the stern rises up and the propeller spins in the air. Since we are parked right over it we hear a great rattling and are almost shaken out of our beds!

Anyway it is fun and I can't see why so many people spoil half their trip, griping about the accommodations. Those who kick the hardest get the best cabins. Those of us who don't bother to fuss are next to the steerage but are a most amiable group, surrounded by the best sports. The only bad result might be that we'll be throttled in our sleep for having such a good time!

We mosey along the coast, anchor in this or that harbor, and native craft come out to sell their wares. Sometimes we go ashore if it looks interesting. In one harbor the skipper let down one of the life-boats (strictly against regulations) so that a group of us could go swimming in the lovely clear blue water.

Since we left Haifa and then Beirut, we have stopped at Tripoli (not the famous one), Alexandrette (Old Aleppo), and Mersina. Then we turned south for Cyprus.

Our first stop there was Famagusta where we had time to prowl around the old walls and visited the famous tower of Othello and Desdemona. A few of us took a car and drove across part of the island which was completely carpeted with gorgeous anemones and poppies. They were so gorgeous we never thought about the opium the latter produced!

We caught up with the Graz at Larnaeka. It seems that besides mules and deck passengers we are now carrying a cargo of raisins, oranges, and asbestos.

April 13, 1929

After leaving Cyprus we sailed around the southern coast of the island and then north to the Turkish coast and stopped at Adalia—an old Crusaders' town. It was a fascinating town full of rock walls, cobbled streets, and gorgeous views. Also there were charming streams cascading down to the sea.

Rhodes was lovely, too, but we didn't have nearly enough time there. The narrow entrance to the harbor was most interesting with its statue of Romulus and Remus atop a pillar on one side and a hart on the other. This, of course, was where the famous Colossus once stood. As the story goes, the bronze statue lay at the bottom of the harbor for years and then was salvaged when the island was besieged and melted up to make cannon balls.

* * * * *

Some awful hotel
Athens, Greece
April 15, 1929

Dearest Family:

Sorry to say I have been ill and in a filthy room filled with cockroaches and no outside window. Addy, bless him, has just managed to get me moved to better quarters and has called in a doctor—bad bronchitis.

Now I'm better and we got to the Acropolis and had a lovely day seeing the Parthenon, Erectheum, etc. We also made a few drives—well worthwhile—but I guess I'm filled up to here with sight-seeing. When I meet you in Paris I'll ask you not to ask me to look at a thing for awhile!

* * * * *

International Hotel
Brindisi, Italy
April 20, 1929

Mother darling:

We arrived here this afternoon after a beautiful twenty-two-hour trip from Athens through the Corinth Canal and the Gulf of Corinth, then across the mouth of the Adriatic. The ship, the Semiramis, named after an Assyrian Queen, is Italian—but what a contrast to the Graz. She looks like a yacht, and what a cuisine! She seemed so large that we wondered why she didn't scrape her paint off going through the fabulously narrow and high-walled Corinth Canal.

The other members of our party are going via the toe of Italy through the Straits of Messina. I regret not seeing Mount Aetna but this shorter trip was fabulous.

tions. Someone said it had been condemned years ago and I

* * * * *

Hotel Romano
Rome
April 24, 1929

Phyl dear:

I'm so glad I saved my energies for the Amalfi Drive and Sorrento. Breathtaking—must go back some day!

Oh, but Rome! I have fallen in love with it. Here we really had enough time to see almost everything without becoming too exhausted. If we had even more time I'd go back to the Borghese gardens and sculpture gallery again and again. I am grateful that I took the course in Italian sculpture at Mount Holyoke. Bernini's David and Daphne and Apollo—!

* * * * *

Hotel de France
Wien, Austria
May 3, 1929

We only had two days in Florence; not nearly enough time to do a fraction of the Uffizi and Pitti Palaces alone. Addy and I looked up beforehand a very few paintings we wanted to concentrate on and that is what we did. I have a vivid impression of one tourist who went through the two galleries with a guide book in his hand. He would glance at a picture, locate the name in his book, and check it off. He'll be able to tell the folks back home that he saw every painting in Florence!

Venice was a disappointment to me—shoddy and down-at-the-heel—and except for St. Mark's Square and a trolley ride down the Grand Canal it left me rather cold. However, I'll readily admit that if I'd had more time there and had not been so travel-weary I might feel far differently about it.

A very few of us extravagantly took a plane up here; three hours, instead of eighteen by train. A beautiful flight through the Italian and Austrian Alps. Our plane was a big (sic) tri-motor job, carrying ten passengers. We were surrounded by rainbows and between clouds could see the gorgeous flower-covered valleys below. (Too young to be worried by the possibility of crashing, it was a memorable first flight for me to recall twenty-five years later.)

Ill and in hospital, der Krankerhaus der Stadt Vien. Sorry to miss Germany but the young Vienese people I met and who were so good to me leave a warm spot in my heart I'll never forget.

* * * * *

"Your sister was so kind to me when I got back to Chicago. I wonder what she thought of me."

"I do remember that long afterwards (I didn't see her in Europe after all) she told me she thought you were very sweet and she wondered why I didn't have enough sense to wait for you and marry you."

"You never would have, would you?"

"Yes, at one point, if you had pressed it—but who knows? I doubt if I would have been good for you. And now your daughter is that age—how lucky you are to have children."

"What about you? You've had no children but you've had quite a life. You were happy in your marriage, weren't you?"

"Very. I've been more fortunate than anyone else I know—in so many ways—"

"Have you ever thought of marrying again?"

"Of course, if I were lucky enough to meet someone. It's not likely. I'll be fifty my next birthday. But, my dear, if I live the rest of my life alone and lonely, I'll have had more of everything in this world than most people I know—more than I've ever earned or deserved."

"If you had only one other man who loved you as I did, you've had more than your share!"

The middle-aged couple rose from the steps of St. Thomas Church and started walking toward Grand Central Terminal. They planned to have a bite at the station before she took her train to Westchester and he took his to New England.

They stopped to consult a timetable and found that her last train was to leave in a few minutes. They kissed goodbye on the suburban platform, nine and a half hours after they had met for lunch under the clock in the Biltmore.

89

CHAPTER V. RETURN TO MEDICINE

(MARY)

Introduction to this chapter was written by Molly in 1973.

In these days, when one reads so much about the quite radical activities of "Women's Lib," I have frequently had numerous thoughts on the subject, going back over the past fifty years and more.

In the first place, my mother, Mary Radford, had been a strong suffragette before and after women got the vote in 1920. She believed in equality of the sexes in general but also felt that women's first and most important job was taking care of the home and the children.

When I entered medical school in 1927 many of mother's friends as well as some of the family disapproved, saying that this was no field for a woman. Mother was proud that I wanted to study medicine and felt that a woman could be just as good a doctor as a man. Her chief objection to my entering the field was that she didn't think I had the physical stamina to stand the rigorous course, as I had had numerous illnesses while growing up.

Quite a number of women had become doctors even in those days and some had been outstanding. Still there were only six women in my entering class out of a hundred starters. Aside from working my way through my first year of medical school plus the ever-present need for constant study, I enjoyed all of it.

In spite of much talk in those days, as well as today, of great prejudice against women in many professional fields, I never experienced any of this! I never heard a snide or derogatory remark from any fellow student or from any of my professors. I was treated with friendly camaraderie in all re-

spects, except possibly by a very few boys who showed rather romantic feelings toward me. My tuition was the same, my grades were based on the kind of work I did. I received no favoritism or downgrading because of my sex. Later, because of illness, travel, etc., I joined other classes of somewhat younger students and was treated in the same manner by them.

In the years to follow, my fellow doctors in Santa Fe not only treated me as an equal and a real friend but paid me the honor of electing me secretary-treasurer and later president of our County Medical Society even though I was the first, and for some time thereafter, the only female doctor in town.

Since that time there have been several women physicians in Santa Fe, some with children as well as husbands. As far as I know, most of these women have done fine jobs and have been accorded much the same treatment as I always had.

Personally, I feel that women in this country have the best of two worlds as long as they are ready, able, and willing to do their job both at home and on the outside.

After her remarkable trip around the world, I had, of course, hoped that Molly might change her mind about continuing medicine. She had an ardent beau, but since he had not yet completed his college course they were not considering marriage. (Quite sensible, I thought.) However, I did want her to marry and have children. With the two of them separated by a good many miles, Molly acquired a new beau! I never did quite understand why my child repeatedly had two at the same time.

In any case, because of the great change in her life due to the travel, she found herself unable to settle down to her medical studies. Being her usual stubborn self, however, she refused to stay with me or Phyllis but insisted in earning her living. She got a job in the admitting office of Billings Hospital. This was somewhat of a relief to me as she wouldn't be working what seemed to me to be twenty-five hours a day.

This job she apparently enjoyed and later said that it was of great benefit to her as she learned much of the patients' and business side of the medical picture. After about six months of this new experience she was ready to resume her studies. Since she was twenty-five years old and obviously knew her own mind I was glad to pay her tuition and living expenses; being only too happy to be able to do so and being relieved that she could concentrate on her chosen work.

In spite of her relatively heavy schedule of studies, Molly had a wonderful time. Aside from the new beau she acquired three other very good friends, all men, of course. (Oh, well, they say there is safety in numbers!) The young men friends were quite remarkable. Two of them were anthropology graduate students, one a most promising physiologist, and one a brilliant biochemist from Peru. They all accomplished their respective work and on off-hours seemed to enjoy life no end—they always seemed to be singing!

Molly returned to the Gulick Camp as a head counsellor that summer of 1930 and I went to Monte D'Or in central France to try a "cure" for my increasingly bad asthma, where I did get considerable relief for months after that. Phyllis was doing splendidly at her new job at Quaker Oats, receiving promotion and more pay and even traveling a lot in her business.

In the autumn Molly returned to the medical studies full of health and enthusiasm in spite of the fact that the "beau" of the previous year had married another woman! Imagine my "puzzlement" over my two girls when I found them together one weekend at our north-shore apartment. Phyllis was in tears and Molly was laughing. Phyllis showed me a letter from a young Englishman she had met during a business trip to England, which was a real love letter. The two had met at a party and had fallen head-over-heels in love at first sight. Molly was holding a telegram telling her that her beau had just married! How does one understand the younger generation?

As the great depression worsened, we Radford "girls" were pretty much on the crest of the wave. My beloved Danish Uncle "Jep" Dau chose that time to give me and two other of his dead wife's nieces a large check in lieu of leaving any bequests in his will. I persuaded him to give an equal amount to my sister, Harriet Dallas. Don had a most successful brass and copper business but was having a very rough time because of the world-wide depression. Actually, it turned out that this gift was heaven-sent to the Dallases —tiding them over until things turned for the better and Don went on to a most successful career heading the well known Revere Copper and Brass Co. for the rest of his active life.

This large windfall made it possible for me to invest in good securities when they were near their lowest cost in those troublesome years.

All went fine for us until January 1931 when Molly developed a very severe "strep" infection. She walked out of a pathology lecture and was put to bed in Billings Hospital in the same building with a temperature of 105 degrees!

Things looked very black, indeed, for some time as the virulent infection caused an acute glomerular nephritis, for which at that time there was no known control or cure.

Gradually, but oh, so slowly, Molly's condition improved and it began to look as though God was good enough to grant her recovery—if not complete, at least partially to where she would be left with a chronic kidney ailment. God was indeed good, and with the devoted care and attentions of several dedicated physicians at Billings she made a complete recovery.

This took six months of hospitalization and a prolonged convalescent period before Molly was once more on her feet.

This chapter is called Return to Medicine. In later years Molly was convinced that her illness which kept her out of school for almost a year and a half was indeed a valued part of her education, not to be regretted.

Interim

(MOLLY)

The day I left the pathology lecture room I knew I was very ill. For some time thereafter I neither knew nor cared much about what was going on. As I began to get somewhat better it dawned on me how much harder all this was on mother than it was on me. It wasn't until years later

94

that I really appreciated the fact that the one who suffers most is the helpless person who stands by watching and waiting for the loved one to live or die.

Also, being in a teaching hospital surrounded by fellow students and professors who were both physicians and friends made my experience a bit different from that of an ordinary patient. The younger of these friends came often to my room. They were concerned about me but also extremely interested in my disease. They didn't hesitate to tell me what my chart said, how my laboratory reports were doing, etc. I was at one and the same time patient and medical student and intern helping to care for myself.

The third thing I learned very well indeed was about illness from the patient's point of view. I think, or at least I hope, that this experience made me a better person and a better doctor.

By the summer of 1931 I was well enough to drive mother east and see her off for France where she was to take further treatment for asthma at Mont D'Or. I was invited to spend some weeks at camp in Maine as a guest with no responsibilities. This I enjoyed to the full until one day when we were camping out in that beautiful countryside a friend brought me a cablegram. My sister, Phyllis, had gone abroad once more on Quaker Oats business. The cable from England said, "Take a fast boat tomorrow to meet your future brother-in-law!"

Phyllis was not in the habit of doing unexpected things on the spur of the moment. It didn't occur to *me* to hesitate. I dashed back to camp with the dirver who had brought the message, threw my belongings into mother's car, and started off for New York. I did stop in Portland to get a visa for my still valid passport and found at the same time that the ship Berengaria was to sail the next morning for Southampton. I drove most of the night, stopped at a friend's to bathe and change into one of my few civilized dresses. I found a garage man who would take me to the pier and store the car.

Walking up to the shipping office on the pier, I startled more than a few people by buying a ticket on the spot and asking for two or three ship's stewards. These young men soon arrived and I loaded them down with clothes on hangers, odd paper bags and cartons full of shoes, etc., and we all paraded up the gangplank! I was halfway across the Atlantic before I caught up with myself!

A radiogram reached me a day or so before we reached Europe, saying, "Get off at Cherbourg. I'll meet you."

Really mystified, but being a dutiful sister, I did just that. There was no one to meet me. However, hoping for the best, I got on the boat train for Paris. Phyllis was there—why, I didn't know. She explained en route to the hotel that she just had to go to see mother in central France and tell her all about her exciting engagement to this wonderful Englishman, George Furness.

She no sooner got me settled in the comfortable little English hotel just off the Champs Elysee than she started to pack her few things to go to see mother. During this brief time she told me (not asked me) to fly to London in six days' time and meet her at the Hotel Berkely—that we would sail for home together on the Duchess of York.

My remonstrances were futile—that I'd just arrived and hoped to see a bit more of France than I had in 1929 and would then go home with mother in a few weeks.

"But Molly, this will be the last time we'll have to travel together! And I'll need company after I leave George!"

My remark that we never *had* traveled together she ignored. I felt that she was somewhat out of her mind! She certainly was sick, lovesick, and I finally gave in. The next six days I rather enjoyed, unexpectedly. It was cold for late August and the few civilized clothes I had with me were strictly for hot weather. I bought a couple of warm garments I could ill afford, and then proceeded to find my way by bus and metro to numerous spots in the city I had always wanted to visit.

Dutifully, on the appointed day I flew to London and taxied to the Berkely. There I asked for my sister and was told she was up in Derbyshire but was expected back that evening or early the next morning. I was allowed to go to her room when I identified myself. There I had a few long thoughts about this absolutely crazy jaunt I'd made to meet my future brother-in-law.

On impulse, I telephoned Southampton and the only person I knew in all of England (besides my missing sister). Fritz Jandrey, my very good friend of the trip around the world was then vice-consul in that port. Fortunately I reached him and then told him my absurd story. Bless him, he came to my rescue. He asked me to come down to Southampton by the first train. He would take me to dinner and a nice evening and the next morning we would go to see the Snyder Cup races (a well known aviation event in those days). My ship, he knew, wouldn't sail until sometime in the early afternoon.

I jumped at the suggestion, left a terse note for Phyllis in the room, and departed. Fritz met my train and took me to the charming home of the consul, who was then away. Fritz had the run of his home and the whole consular office. We had a lovely dinner and a wonderful chat, catching up on each other's news of the past two years. When it came time to retire, although the consul's house was a large one it never occurred to either of us that I should spend the night there. (How different things are now in 1972, forty years later!)

Fritz telephoned practically every hotel in the large city to find a room for me. I ended up in the bridal suite of a push hotel—the only room available because of the masses of people who had come to Southampton for the air show the next day.

The next day didn't dawn! There was a pea-soup fog with visibility zero. Fritz phoned to say that there not only would be no Cup races but that he had to clear two ships that morning which had been off schedule because of the fog. He was most apologetic not to be able to escort me anywhere but said he'd do his best to get to the Duchess of York before we sailed.

Being quite used to being "stood up" in one way or another in the past week I packed up my few possessions—I'd bought a cardboard suitcase in Paris, so had gotten rid of my paper bags and cartons—and had a leisurely breakfast of coffee and rolls. After paying thirteen dollars for my "bridal suite" I had barely enough money left to get to the ship. If Phyllis, who had the tickets, didn't show up I had visions of either being a stowaway or of washing dishes all the way across the Atlantic!

Once aboard the ship, they not only let me on among the see-er-offs, but let me into the cabin Phyllis had reserved when I showed them my passport to convince them I was a Miss Radford. I ambled up top-side to watch for the first boat-train from London. I watched in vain. I repeated this maneuver three times. In between scanning the crowds I explored the ship pretty thoroughly. She was a beauty, with appointments and lines almost like a large yacht. Meanwhile, becoming almost desperate about being so deserted, I spent my last twenty-five cents on a glass of sherry in the bar. (Had I been a bit older and bolder I should probably have gotten drunk and signed my sister's name to the chits.) Still, I had some reservations. The skipper might not hire a drunken dishwasher, might not pay any stewardess enough to cover the chits, or he might just put me off before sailing and leave me penniless on a foreign shore. About the time I was wondering if Scotland Yard could and would help me find Phyllis, the last boat train pulled in.

Trailing along near the end of the crowd walking toward the gangplank I spotted a snappy looking blue hat and behind it a man who looked about seven feet tall. (He turned out to be six feet four.) As my sister and her beau reached the deck, the half-hour "all ashore that are going ashore" rang out. George smiled broadly as we shook hands and said,

"Let's all have a farewell drink together."

I muttered something about "Hail and farewell."

As long as George lived he always said that my first words to him were, "This is the way to the bar!"

As the ship pulled away from the pier my weeping sister hung over the rail, waving to her tall beloved who stood at the end of the dock. Suddenly I realized that standing next to George was an equally tall man who looked very familiar. He had a bouquet of bright red carnations clutched in one hand while waving with the other. It was Fritz!! He later wrote me that he'd reached our ship almost an hour before sailing time. Due to the crowds and my constantly moving and looking about the ship, we had missed connections completely. I never did ask him why he hadn't left the flowers in the Radford cabin. I appreciated the one friend I had in all of Europe too much!

The less said about the voyage home the better. September weather was foul and cold. The beautiful ship was a poor sailer, tossing about like a cork. Phyllis, who was reputedly a good sailor who had never been seasick stayed in her bunk practically the entire eight days—lovesick, not seasick. I wasn't at all sick but bored and disgusted; among the other travelers I didn't meet one, male or female, whom I would recall five minutes later. "Our last wonderful trip together—umph!"

Unfortunately that wasn't the end of it. On arrival at Montreal I fully expected my sister to go to New York with me to get the family car and perhaps see a few theatres together and perhaps traipse about the city as we had on occasion in the mid-twenties, before she had to return to her job. I, of course, expected to await mother's arrival in order to drive her back to the Midwest. Instead, Phyllis stated that she had to go to Chicago directly and back to her job. I suspected that all the excitement of becoming engaged and meeting George's family in Derbyshire had caused her to stay abroad longer than had been planned. The lovesick sister departed, and I entrained for New York.

I had two or three pleasant days with an old friend, Helen Cowles, in her delightful penthouse. However, a cable from mother arrived saying that she was sailing for home sooner than planned and would arrive at Montreal shortly. Helen, good sport that she was, offered to drive with me to Canada to meet mother. It was a lovely trip with the autumn coloring and we both enjoyed it. However, our dates were slightly confused and when we reached Montreal we learned that mother's ship had just arrived in port. I drove Helen, that most amiable of gals, to the station to catch a night train back home, and went to greet mother.

On arrival at the pier I was dismayed to find that only residents of Montreal were allowed to disembark that evening. Others were to wait until morning. I could see mother at the rail above me and at that I "blew my top." Inside I was seething with frustration but outwardly I had sense enough to pull an act.

To an official on the pier I said, "This is the first time I've been in a big city. I'm all alone and my mother is up there. Please won't you let her off as I wouldn't know where to go or what to do, otherwise. I even produced a few tears, and tired and dirty as I was and without makeup I guess I appeared rather young and helpless. In any case mother and bags came down the gangplank. The solicitous official kindly said that mother could deal with customs when we crossed into the United States.

After a night in some hotel we made a record drive for those days back to Chicago in time for me to register once more in a new class in medical school.

Years later when I regaled my nieces with the tale of my crazy trip to meet their father, Phyllis denied or at least misremembered most of it. George's only comment was, "The first time I met your Aunt Molly her only words were, 'This is the way to the bar!!' " By that time I was amused and well knew my brother-in-law's outrageous sense of humor.

Introduction to New Mexico

(MOLLY)

After a couple of months in medical school I was much distressed to find that I could not continue my studies. Partially due to the many medications I had taken most of that year of 1931, I suffered extensive allergies and developed giant hives. I was one big "itch." My kind and concerned doctors Emmet Bay, Philip Miller, and O. H. Robertson decided I should drop out once more and go west. Fortunately for me they recommended the Valley Ranch in New Mexico near Santa Fe. Two of them had stayed there and felt it would be an ideal place for me.

In November I got off the Santa Fe Chief at Glorieta. I could see nothing but high red clay banks on each side of the train. Then Wayne Wilson, the manager of the ranch, appeared, picked up my bags, and escorted me to his station wagon. It was a short drive to the ranch and I fell in love

100

with the countryside immediately. Although very different from the gorgeous Teton country of Wyoming which I had adored in 1925-26, it had the same great lure for me and I knew that I would love my sojourn there even though it was winter.

No one had thought to tell me that the altitude was seven thousand feet, so I had blithely packed bathing suits, shorts, etc. However, the skies were blue and the exceedingly low humidity made any cold barely noticeable. The air was invigorating and soon I was riding horseback along interesting trails in the mountains and feeling better by the minute. The peace, quiet, and warmth of the Wilson family and the few winter guests made my four months there quite perfect. I hated to leave in February but Phyllis's wedding was approaching in March and I was thoroughly well and still had over two years of medical school ahead of me. I thought that someday I would return for visits but never dreamed that it was to be my future home—NEW MEXICO!

* * * * *

Daughters Gone but Not Lost

(MARY)

March 1932 in Chicago was miserable, weatherwise deep in snow and slush but for the three Radford women it was full of the flurry of trouseau shopping, bride and bridesmaids selection of gowns, and fittings. Depression prices were a boon to us in more ways than one. Phyllis acquired more and more beautiful clothes than I'd ever dreamed to see my daughter wear. In the finest of Chicago shops; Blum's and McAvoy's and others sales women fell all over themselves to sell their lovely clothes, linens, etc., to someone who was in a position to buy anything in those days.

Hattie and Don Dallas graciously provided the setting for the lovely wedding, the ceremony being in the charming Episcopal church in Winnetka and the beautiful reception at their magnificent home overlooking Lake Michigan. Emily Johnson, the wonderful friend and helper who was with the

Dallas family for so many years, discovered that the distracted groom-to-be and his best man had neglected to unpack the groom's morning coat from the suitcase it had been packed in for well over two weeks on their trip from England. However, she sponged and pressed it in the nick of time.

Coming down the aisle of the church following the marriage, George broke all tradition and grabbed Phyllis in his arms to kiss her—enchanting the entire assembly. Just before the first guests arrived for the reception, Molly retrieved the austere rolled, black umbrella which the groom had thoughtfully hung on the handsome Italian marble fireplace mantel in the oval dining room next to the wedding feast, and all went well.

Since I had no idea when I'd see my older daughter again, Molly and I drove to New York, taking the best man, Len Wright, with us to see the newlyweds off on their ship. En route we stopped in Washington for Len to see the sights and Molly and I had the pleasure of seeing the Howard Chandler Christy painting of "our Rob Roy" hanging in the tourist section of the White House.

An amusing incident happened when we were all staying for two days in the Barclay Hotel in New York. Molly and George happened to be alone in the elevator with the operator. George was talking at a great rate to Molly. When he stepped off the elevator at his floor the operator turned to Molly and said, in his Brooklyn accent,

"What language was that man speaking?"

Molly replied, in amusement, "Why, English."

The elevator boy turned his back on Molly in disgust and disbelief! However, when Molly related this incident to me later we were both sobered by the thought that Phyllis was leaving us for good to live in a faraway country even though it wasn't quite as "foreign" to us as it was to the boy from Brooklyn. Neither of us suspected then that we would be fortunate enough to span that three thousand miles numerous times so that we should be able to keep in close contact for the rest of our lives.

That summer Molly returned to medical school for the fourth and final time. She was full of good health and her work was completely absorbing, as she was then in her clinical years working directly with patients. I returned to live with my dear uncle in his lovely southside home. I was glad to be reasonably near the university so that my younger daughter could drop in briefly on occasion.

* * * * *

Serious Life with a Capital L

(MOLLY)

It didn't take long to become lost in the world of medicine. For three months during my first real experience as a "doctor" I happily took the opportunity of being a substitute intern in the pediatric department. I loved working with the ill and injured children, who for the most part are usually the "best patients" to care for. For some time after that experience I was sure that I wanted to be a pediatrician for the rest of my active life.

A bit later, in the cold weather, I was ready to go into obstetrics. This meant that I would live in the intern's quarters at the hospital and be on twenty-four-hour call for delivering babies in the south-side slums. In between calls we, of course, had lectures and helped in the hospital delivery rooms. Other students and I were on a roster, taking turns as the calls came in. Each of us went out with a more experienced young intern. If both of us got involved in a difficult case we could always call in for "the wrecking crew," an experienced obstetrician with an equally experienced obstetrical nurse. Since most births are normal, my slightly more knowledgeable companion would usually let me take charge of the delivery.

Out of over twenty babies I ushered into the world I still recall several unusual or amusing incidents:

The slovenly woman had made no preparations for her delivery at home even though she had been given detailed instructions well ahead of time and it was her third child. Since "her time" had not yet come, I was left alone for a short while when my senior partner had gone for a cup of

103

coffee. I had persuaded a reluctant woman in the neighboring apartment to take on the two screaming small children who were hovering around the bed. The messy room, however, was not quiet as the impatient patient loudly proclaimed her suffering even when she was experiencing no contractions. She was wasting her energies, her breath, assaulting my eardrums and wearing my patience thin.

"Shut up! You aren't having that much pain," I said.

The surprised woman looked up at the first woman doctor she had ever seen, stopped yelling, and said to me, "Have you had a baby?"

Lying stoutly, I said, "Certainly. I have three children. Now get on with your job."

At that moment the intern had just come in the door. He stared at me with dropped jaw.

After an easy and successful delivery, and some of the mess in the room had been cleared up—there was no husband or any other man to be seen—now that the noise had stopped, the neighbor poked her head in the door and said she would help with the children.

As Paul and I drove back to the hospital he turned to me and said, "By damn, there is something to be said for female doctors, after all!" Then he added, "Was that really true, what you told that gal?"

I said, "Of course it wasn't—but it worked, didn't it?"

* * * * *

On other occasions we young "apprentice obstetricians" were sometimes urged to drink a toast to the new arrival. Even in those dark, depression days there were a few young and hopeful fathers who had jobs. The drinks, offered at practically any time of day or night depending on the arrival time of the infant, consisted mainly of home-made wine which was usually not very good but probably safer than "bath-tub gin." The idea of ingesting what was possibly methyl alcohol did not appeal to medical students at any time. Even the best of liquors would not have interested them at odd hours of the morning. We usually got around the problem by saying that we never drank "on duty" or by pretending to sample the libation in order not to hurt any feelings. A few parents asked our names, and I suspect one or two Lithuanian, Italian, or Slovak girls in the southwest side of Chicago (women now) carry the name of Molly!

One case I have not forgotten was in a quite neat and clean place which had practically no furniture in it. Chairs, tables, etc., had been sold for food or else had been burned in the stove for warmth. The solicitous father, however, had troubled to sterilize a batch of newspapers, according to instructions from the Hull House organization. In this case there was at least something clean on which to place instruments and in which to wrap the new child.

On one "baby case," experienced by a friend of mine, another female or "hen medic" had a rather disturbing time of another sort. This tired girl returned to her car after a long, hard delivery case. She found the ancient but serviceable vehicle dismantled—there was nothing left but the chassis. Tires, engine, everything had been stripped clean, including an old but warm muskrat coat which the girl had forgotten in her rush to get to her patient.

She walked through the tough Sicilian neighborhood in the cold predawn to Hull House to report. The head of that wonderful outfit, "Katie" Kemper, happened to be on duty. On hearing the girl's story, Katie strode out of the building and started combing the neighborhood until she found what she was looking for, a dingy speakeasy. There she was told where she could find the "boss" of a ring of gangsters at that hour. Soon Katie was confronting Al Capone! She told him in no uncertain terms what had happened, that the girl "doctor" had taken good care of one of his own people and had delivered a fine baby. The result? Orders were sent out to the "gang" and within about three hours the young woman's car was rehabilitated, complete with new engine, new tires, as well as a few extras. To top it off, there was a fine new fur coat on the seat. From that day forward, so far as I know, no medical student or his car was molested in that section of town!

I well recall, to my great pleasure, another delivery in a very decent home where both parents were happily expecting their first child. The father had had a job but after losing it through no fault of his own there was no money for a doctor. The pregnant woman was very cooperative and the prospec-

105

tive father had built a nice little bassinet for the newcomer.

Jim, my partner in charge, and I examined the woman. All seemed in order but there was a bit of time to wait, so Jim retired to the living room couch for some much needed sleep and told me to call him when the babe had arrived.

About an hour later I walked into the living room, nudged Jim awake, and proudly showed him a fine baby boy, about seven pounds in weight. Jim sleepily said, "That's fine, Molly. Carry on, and wake me when you are finished."

Rather hesitantly I said, "But there is another baby in there."

Jim's reply was, "All you people new in this job think you're going to have twins someday! Don't bother me."

Dutifully, I returned to the bedroom. I was quite certain I was right, but since everything seemed to be going well I said no more.

In about an hour I went back, this time with a seven-and-a-half-pound boy. Jim sat up and stared. "You're kidding, that's the same baby!" However, he strode into the other room and stopped short when he saw the other infant all dressed and in the new crib. He knew full well, just as I did, that in the case of twins or any complications of any sort student "doctors" were supposed to call in the "wrecking crew," a team of more experienced doctor and nurse, some of whom were always on call.

The new mama smiled up at us from her clean bed and papa was busily emptying out a bureau drawer for the unexpected addition. I thanked heaven that this hadn't happened in a family where there were already five or six, or perhaps ten children!

Jim was very silent as we picked up our things and prepared to leave; knowing he would have to report this and that he would get the devil for not calling in. However, since all had gone so smoothly, he had the grace to tell me when we got in the car that I'd done a fine job, and admitted ruefully that he himself had never delivered twins although he had been in obstetrics for many months.

These were my only twins, and in a way I was sorry that they were both boys. Otherwise one of them might have carried my name!

An interesting sequel to the above: the next time Jim and I happened to be teamed on the same assignment we walked into a Latvian home. Lying on the kitchen table was a very large and very pregnant woman. Numerous friends and relatives were in the room but not one could speak English. There were several small children present, some of whom obviously belonged to our patient.

As we prepared for the delivery, Jim sternly waved all the bystanders out of the room except one woman who would not budge. We both suspected that she had attended many more births than either or perhaps both of us had, so we said nothing and so did she. Jim carefully palpated the huge abdomen. As in the case of many of these families, the woman had not attended a prenatal clinic, so there was no record to go on. As the patient was obviously having severe contractions and had been in labor for some time, Jim motioned for me to administer some ether. Then he seated himself at the other end of the table to await developments. Had there been a phone anywhere nearby or had there been anyone who spoke English I'm quite certain he would have called the "wrecking crew." However, labor had progressed too far to allow us to leave the woman.

I secretly hoped that Jim would have his first pair of twins—maybe triplets, by the look of that mound. Before too long, a bit rested by a slight amount of anesthetic, the patient gave a good hard push and a normal baby arrived, followed by the afterbirth. Jim attended the child and handed it to the silent woman. He then turned back to the patient whose abdomen appeared almost as large as it had before, signaling me to maintain a very slight anesthesia. So we all waited—twins sometimes are born at some intervals apart.

I lost track of time but it wasn't too long before there was a chattering at the door. A new face appeared, an older woman who said, "I spik Inglish, what is matter? What wait for?"

Jim pointed to the abdomen. The newcomer said calmly, "No wait for it," and pointing to the great bulge, added, "She been there ten years—lots of babies, but she no come!"

Jim and I looked at each other. Without a word we cleaned up things and by the time we carried the woman back to her bed, with some needed help from the audience who had returned, the patient was wide awake. With her newest offspring beside her, and the "she" who had been there ten years still in place, she waved us a cheerful goodby!

I doubt that Jim ever reported the huge benign fibroid tumor which had given no trouble in ten years, in spite of existing in extremely close contact with five normally developing fetuses. Such a woman would never go into a hospital for surgery in any case.

One other episode remembered from those days—the saddest one, in some ways, occurred one bitter night when my intern boss, Bob, and I climbed five flights of stairs in a tumbled-down tenement. We found our patient lying on a bed of rags on the floor. There was not one stick of furniture in the room, just a few wooden boxes and cartons and a tiny pot-bellied stove which gave out practically no heat. The only running water was at a "community" sink down the hall. Fortunately there were no children besides the one about to arrive. The man who led us there and the woman uttered no complaint and seemed resigned to their desperate situation. Bob and I did the best we could and were lucky that it was an easy delivery. The baby, a girl, seemed healthy and I wrapped her up as best I could in a few rags and placed her beside the wan mother. Bob and the father went down the stairs where there was a phone. Bob reported to Hull House the situation. Not one speck of food or clothing other than what the man and wife were wearing was present in that hopeless household. Bob was told that someone from that amazing place (Hull House) would be on the way shortly with necessities. We waited in that stark room until a visiting nurse arrived with clothes and food and a promise that another charity organization would come with some odds-and-ends of furniture. Before we left, the new father, accompanying us down the long flights of stairs, expressed his appreciation and said, "I'm so glad the baby is a girl. In these terrible times girls can usually find jobs when men can't!"

Poor souls. They would have to wait quite a long time for this one to become a breadwinner!

CHAPTER VI. MOVE TO SANTA FE

(MARY)

Much to my relief, Molly's health remained fine during her last three years in medicine in spite of her arduous weeks delivering babies in the slums, when I saw nothing of her. Phyllis had her first baby, Diana, in early 1933 and naturally I went over to see my first grandchild that summer before going to Mont D'Or for my asthma. I did persuade Molly to go over too for a few weeks and she enjoyed a short visit with the Furnesses and saw more of England than she had on her two preceding crazy few days there.

She took an informal jaunt around some of Scotland, walking a good part of the way. She told us later with much amusement that the Scottish people she met refused to believe that she was an American because they had never seen one who walked anywhere. She also had about a month in Paris staying with a French family, which gave her a chance to see more of that beautiful city and to brush up on her one foreign language, which was a good change from her deep involvement in medicine.

Uncle was doing fine with his excellent household help during the time when we were both away. However, Molly took my place in that lovely home during most of the several months I was abroad. That was a very pleasant change for her after her sojourns in interns' quarters and days and nights in the wretchedly poor ghettoes of the southwest side of the city.

When I returned Molly once more took a small apartment and concentrated on her very strenuous last year of medical school. It was soon apparent that she had another heavy beau! Gene was a White Russian who was brilliant and had great charm. He had transferred from a Denver school and they were taking the same courses, so did much of their studying together. Between the two of them they had made numerous friends among some of the fine professors in and out of the medical field, and it seemed to be an enriching experience for both of them.

In the summer of 1934 they received their four-year medical certificates together after most strenuous weeks of long examinations. Their M.D. degrees would not come until they had served a given time interning and/or in research work. Gene took a regular internship in Billings Hospital. Molly, who I thought was going into Pediatrics, suddenly announced that Gene had a most interesting research project started in the Physiology Department under Dr. A. J. Carlson. He had persuaded her to take over that work instead of interning.

Personally I was glad that she was to enter that field of research as I was sure it would be less strenuous than active clinical medicine. She worked on that project involving early investigation into the role of Vitamin C in tuberculosis for a year, and Gene and Molly received their M.D. degrees in 1935. Meanwhile Gene had wangled a fellowship from the Belgian Relief foundation started by Herbert Hoover following his excellent relief undertaking in Europe. The former President had saved some two million dollars and put it into a fund for exchange fellowships between American and Belgian students.

I didn't know too much about the arrangements except that Gene was to go abroad while Molly finished the research work. Then she was to go to Belgium the following year. They seemed so devoted to each other and to their common interest that I felt sure they would marry eventually.

In the spring of 1936 Phyllis had a second daughter, Elizabeth, called Beebi, and I couldn't wait for summer in order to go to see her. Molly was happily finishing her piece of research and I was proud when her paper was accepted to be presented at the National Tuberculosis Association meeting in New Orleans where she went to present it. What I didn't know was that Gene, in Europe, was having a fine time and had written Molly to carry on with another year of research before going abroad.

Molly must tell the next part of the story.

(MOLLY)

One fine day in late May I was pondering on how the next stage of the research work was progressing. Both Dr. Carlson and I felt that there was not too much point in continuing on the same lines. We had proven to our satisfaction that Vitamin C (ascorbic acid) did improve the blood picture in patients far gone with tuberculosis but it certainly didn't cure their disease. Dr. Henry Sweeney, the head pathologist at the municipal TB sanitorium where I had been working agreed with us. However, the money for the project had been appropriated and my assistants were busy. There was little for me to do until it was time to evaluate further results.

At this point my entire future was about to be altered, although little did I know it at the time. My phone rang and a friend, Polly Day from St. Louis, said,

"Molly, I just got into town. I'm driving a new station wagon out to Dad's ranch on the Pecos. How about coming along and helping me drive it?"

"Pecos, New Mexico?" I exclaimed. "When are you leaving? How long will you be gone?"

"Oh, I plan to get off in two or three hours. Expect I'll stay at the ranch about ten days and then return by train. Come on. It should be lovely out there now. It'll do you good!"

On the spur of the moment I decided that it was a good time for me to take a vacation. I told Polly I'd meet her at a certain time and place, called my assistants to carry on as they were doing, and went to Uncle's house to pack up a few things.

Dear Uncle had died the year before at age eighty-nine but mother and I had been asked to stay on in the house until the estate was settled. I happily joined Polly and we started west. Mother was already in England but I felt no need to inform her of this brief vacation. Polly was the daughter of long-time friends of mother's, the Tom Wyles, who lived in Highland Park, north of Chicago. They had had

111

the New Mexico ranch for about ten years and usually spent their summers there when Polly and her sister and brothers were growing up. The ranch, I knew, was in the lovely Pecos valley just twenty-five miles from Santa Fe and very near the Valley Ranch where I had spent the winter five years before.

As we drove into that well remembered country I took a deep breath and felt as if I had come home. We stayed at the Wyles' for a few days, but not wanting to impose, I moved over to the dude ranch for several days, getting reacquainted with the nice Wilson family and riding over those beloved horseback trails. Shortly I had an attack of acute pleurisy. Chest pains had been bothering me for some weeks but I had paid little attention to them. However, this was severe enough to send me to St. Vincent Hospital in Santa Fe.

There I had about a week in which to have some long thoughts. I had my M.D. degree. I loved this country. I'd had enough of big-city living. Gene's letters had grown increasingly less frequent and less insistent on my going over to Europe. His latest, forwarded to me, said he was taking off for the Belgian Congo and that he was writing a book. It didn't appear that he was missing me any more than I was missing him! I was my own woman!

As soon as I got out of the hospital I went to La Fonda Hotel and made my plans. I found through new friends a charming one-room apartment in Sarah McComb's lovely old home and rented it for the balance of the summer. Soon I was on my way to wind up my project and to pack up all of my belongings. On my arrival I found a letter from mother who was happily enjoying Phyllis's and George's new home in Buckinghamshire and her adorable granddaughters. I also found a parcel from Gene, in Belgium, containing two very handsome gifts. These I promptly mailed to a long-time friend of his in Denver with Gene's microscope and many books which he had left with me the year before, saying that since he and I had parted company I no longer wished to be responsible for anything of his. At the same time I wrote Gene a final letter telling him I had turned down the Belgium fellowship, would not see him again, and wished him luck.

With that off my chest I consulted both of my dear mentors,

Dr. A. J. Carlson at the University and Dr. Henry Sweeney at the Chicago Municipal Tuberculosis Sanitorium. I told each my story. Dr. Carlson agreed that my assistants could easily wind up the loose ends of the research project and thoroughly approved of my going west and making a new life for myself in a healthier environment.

Then this wise gentleman added, "You know, Molly, De-Savitch is a charming, brilliant man, with enormous possibilities. If I hadn't thought so I would never have gone with you and him to vouch for him when he got his citizenship papers. However, I'm beginning to suspect there is a serious flaw in his character. For that reason I'm delighted to see you getting out from under his influence. Go, and God bless you!"

Dr. Sweeney said much the same thing, but he, as a practicing physician as well as being a fine pathologist, examined my chest and finding a friction rub and seeing a pleural spot in the X ray, said, "Get as far away as you can. Leave any further work in this line to us old 'poops' who already have tuberculosis."

So with conscience clear I went back to Santa Fe for good.

Both men were right. Some time later Gene got into serious trouble more than once. He even wrote me threatening me with public exposure of some of my more injudicious letters to him if I didn't go to Washington to testify in his behalf when he was being sued by a prominent official in Washington, D.C. At this time I was married to Bill Martin and happily settled in my permanent home. I was a bit frightened but couldn't see how a few old love letters could help him or hurt me. In any case I wrote to Drs. Carlson, Sweeney, and also Dr. Dallas Phemister, head of surgery at Billings who was also a good friend of mine. Gene had interned under him some years before. All three of these distinguished men wrote me to forget the entire matter. Each of them said they had enough damaging information about Gene to stop him in his tracks! (I kept those letters for years until I heard that Gene had died.)

Two "loose ends:"

1. One day I had a phone call from a Washington newspaper reporter in Denver. He asked me a lot of questions

about Eugene DeSavitch. I answered most of them noncommittally but did state, when asked, that Gene was not a "quack;" that he had graduated from medical school and that I knew he was a citizen of the United States. When the reporter wanted to come down to interview me I flatly refused and said that I knew no more about the doctor.

2. Some time after I'd settled in New Mexico I received another parcel. This contained a handsome carved elephant and an unusual teakwood carved Belgian Congo head plus a leather cushion cover made of various African animal skins. These, I blush to say, I acknowledged but never returned—I'd paid *so* much "duty" for them that I felt I'd bought them!

3. After my *Bill Martin* book was accepted for publication in 1958, Gene wrote me, care of a former mutual friend, that if I would send him a copy, he would honor me by reciprocating with his one published book! I replied on a postcard mailed in London where we both happened to be at the time, that I was sure it would not be a fair trade as his book must be far better than mine!

I heard later that although he had married a very rich widow at some point, he died in London alone and miserable at age 58 or 59.

CHAPTER VII. BILL MARTIN

(MARY)

My unpredictable child! Molly was 31 years old when I got her letter telling of this drastic move. She was certainly a grown woman and had been out from under my wing for some years. Furthermore, thanks to Katie's money and dear Uncle's generosity, I had been able to give her a decent amount of money equal to what I'd given Phyllis at the time of her marriage. Molly had not spent this as she had been earning her living during her research years. Still, as every mother knows, she was still my child and always would be.

This move, two thousand miles away from our home base in Chicago in the opposite direction from the one Phyllis had made four years before, left me quite stunned. However, I was relieved that, with threatened TB, she was out of the dirty city. Furthermore, I realized that I had been fortunate in having my daughters with or near me far longer than most. So, I got on with *my* job.

Uncle's will had left all of his accumulated wealth at his death to fine Chicago charities. The estate was being probated, but his Danish nephew, who had received the same gift of money as we nieces on Aunt Harriet's side had, was trying to break the will. The courts, fortunately, wouldn't allow it, but the physical household things were left to me and the above-mentioned nephew to be amicably divided between us and our respective relatives.

Back in the lovely home I found that Fred had persuaded the chauffeur, maid, and cook to join him in the suit; much to their later regret, as I believe they even lost the generous bequests Uncle had made for them. With some difficulty I avoided any real controversy over the division of "things." I had lived with them, Fred hadn't. I knew the value, both

115

real and sentimental, of the things to my side of the family. So I sat placidly by while Fred picked out most of the more ostentatiously elegant rugs, beds, chairs, etc. It paid off, as I ended up with most of the things precious to me. Among these were fine English china, a good part of the handsome Versailles flat silver, and enough of the smaller valuable oriental rugs, and furniture. These would be enough to furnish any home I or my family would ever need or want. I had them sent to storage after giving Hattie and a couple of cousins their choice of pieces.

This all took some doing and it was mid-fall by the time I started west. I couldn't take the Chicago winters and had started going to California for the worst of the cold weather where several of my old Wisconsin friends had already moved. Naturally I went to Santa Fe first. Molly had by that time sublet the "Casa Gallina," a remodeled chicken house on Sarah McComb's property. It had two bedrooms and was most cosy and comfortable.

Molly had spent the intervening time in hard study for her State Board Medical examinations for New Mexico and had passed them. She had also made many new friends among Santa Fe doctors and others. It immediately became obvious that Bill Martin, the chief criminal investigator for the New Mexico State Police, was a very special friend. He was obviously in love with Molly. His former wife, who had been an invalid for some years, had died in her parent's home in Canada some time before.

Molly and Bill had met the previous summer at the Valley Ranch, and by the time I arrived he seemed to be ever present, as so many of her previous beaux had been over the years. All of their mutual friends admired and/or adored him. I liked him immediately but he was so alien to my Middlewest-Anglo-oriented background that I couldn't visualize him as being in any way comparable to the sort of people I'd ever known. Gene, Molly's former beau, had been foreign-born also but he had had the polish, beautiful command of language (Russian, French, and English) acquired from an excellent education, as well as good looks and charm.

116

It wasn't till later when Molly revealed to me some hard facts about Gene's lack of integrity that I knew how little the surface polish and charm really counted. In my inner-most being I had known that from the experience of my own disastrous marriage. However, at the time I couldn't recon-cile myself to seeing my daughter marrying this "diamond in the rough."

In addition, the relatively wild, barren open spaces of New Mexico, plus Bill's rather bloodcurdling tales of criminal in-vestigations, so put me off that I didn't like anything about New Mexico—in spite of its lovely mountains, gorgeous sunny blue skies, and relaxed, informal way of life. When Bill and Molly drove me out the old Santa Fe Trail to see his one hundred acres of land just south of town where they planned to build their home, the relative desolateness and remoteness of the area seemed like the mountains of the moon. I felt as if my younger daughter would be much more lost to me than Phyllis who was three thousand miles across the ocean.

I spent a "white night" January 15, 1937. The next noon they were married in front of the fireplace in the "chicken house" (the Casa Gallina) by the Reverend James Kinsolving (later the Episcopal Bishop of New Mexico), with me and Caroline Dozier, Molly's "Indian Maid," as witnesses. It was done and I wrote to Chicago to have the storage people send out all my worldly goods to Santa Fe when the Martins' new pueblo-style home was to be completed. I had had no home base for years, and this was the only thing to do. I left for California the next day in a blizzard and promised to return in June on my way back to friends in Chicago and then England.

It was considerably later that Molly told me she had known how I felt and had been sad for me but not for her-self. Forgotten were her plans to resume medicine!

CHAPTER VIII. BACK TO COUN-
TRY LIVING 1937-1940

(MOLLY)

Before my marriage to Bill I had started drawing plans for a home to be built on that "desolate, remote" land of his. During the previous years when Bill had been paying, in installments, for that piece of property a number of his friends had driven out there and told him, "Bill, you must be losing your mind. With your wife in the hospital most of the time and bills piling up, you are working yourself to death for what? Buying that godforsaken land, way out of town where no one would think of living!"

Nevertheless, Bill continued to have men drill a 350 foot well on the highest part of the property hoping that someday he would have a home, orchard and peace and quiet with lovely views of the mountains in all directions.

Some of his friends, visiting "Los Pinones" in later years said to us, "How did you happen to be so lucky as to have this lovely country place so near to town?"!

My initial detailed plans were finished for the house by early February and a contractor started building. At the same time we had ordered a large windmill and gravity tank which Bill's good friend, Jim Mathieson, was installing. I spent most of my waking hours at the building site and Bill joined me at every possible time when he was not working on his own private investigations. (By that time he had resigned from the New Mexico State Police which is recounted in BILL MARTIN, AMERICAN.)

Our first contretemps came when I said, one day, "With this deep well and a promised good flow of water, why don't we have a swimming pool? There is a good slope of land right here near the tank so it wouldn't take too much digging, and it could serve as a reservoir being well above where the house is going up?"

Bill's reply was, "Well I do plan to have an extra reservoir tank back here in the piñons. I want to have a nice orchard and later raise chickens when I retire. But, a swimming pool would be far too expensive."

"How big a tank do you have in mind?"

"Oh, about thirty or forty thousand gallons."

"Would you mind if I get bids on a plain concrete swimming pool?"

"Of course not, go ahead."

I did, and the upshot was that my figure for a fifty thousand gallon concrete pool was five hundred dollars less than his for a forty thousand gallon metal tank! Soon we had a hard-working Spanish American with two horses and a large scoop digging out a fifty by thirty foot excavation —three feet deep at the upper end and eight feet at the lower. This we lined with reinforced concrete walls using the men who were pouring cement foundations for the house. By the time the windmill, with its sixteen foot head, had filled the elevated gravity tank the overflow pipe at the top of the latter was starting to pour water into the first swimming pool of the area!

By the time the walls of the house and the garage-stable were going up Bill and I were building a three apartment dog house and walling in the scaffold under the gravity tank with second hand bricks from a demolished building. I doubt if there is a spot on the place where Bill and I did not have a picnic sandwich during those weeks of supervising all the construction. One of our proudest days was sitting on a board in our present living room in front of the first fireplace in which we were burning scraps of wood. The fire burned brightly with no smoke entering the room though there was no roof over us and no glass in the windows!

Spring was coming on and Bill hauled many wheelbarrows of surface soil to the front of the unfinished main house, levelled it by hand and started a lawn. We also laid some flagstone walks and planted a few trees and shrubs about the place then built a retaining wall around the exposed end of the pool with rocks we brought in our old station wagon from nearby arroyas.

On May fourth we moved into our four-room house with Bill's furniture plus the things mother had sent out from Chicago. Caroline Dozier had made curtains and helped us get settled. Then she left us, to my great regret, for a better paying job in town. A Spanish-American friend, Rueben Martinez and his two sons fenced in a good part of the property for a pasture. (Bill had saved Rueben's boy from the electric chair some years before by proving he had not committed a murder up in Velarde on the Rio Grande.)

As soon as the pasture was enclosed and we had built a wooden corral next to the stable, Wayne Wilson of Valley ranch gave Bill a wonderful old horse named Speck who was soon part of the "family." We ordered two collie pups, Susie and Dusty, who were presumably descendants of some of father's dogs of many years before.

The morning after we moved in we had a dreadful shock! Bill had risen early, as usual, and toured the place. He found everything in order. However when he went out after breakfast he returned on the run saying, "Something is awfully wrong. There is no water running from the tank into the pool. I know the tank was full last night and the windmill is whirling like mad!"

We phoned Jim Mathieson who came out immediately. The rod of the pump was working fine, the tank *was* full to the top but there was no water flowing! At least we had sixty thousand gallons in the pool and seven thousand in the gravity tank and thanked heaven for that!

A few hours later Jim phoned us and said, "I think I've found the answer. Did you know that there is a large house being started about a quarter of a mile to the east of you —between you and the foothills? I drove in there and they have a very deep well with a temporary pump on it producing water for a lot of men making adobes—the workmen seem to let the water run all day. I can't believe that a well that far from yours could affect you—but if it is on the same underground stream it is possible. I suggest you start up your windmill about an hour after five o'clock when the men have quit work and see what happens."

Bill did exactly that and about two hours later we saw the blessed water flowing once more! The only thing to do was for Jim to come back, dismantle the windmill, pull the rod and start drilling deeper. He and his dedicated workmen did so and after about a week or ten days—one hundred and seventeen feet deeper—a new underground stream was located! They had worked night and day and you can bet that Bill and I didn't sleep very well as we listened to that drill pounding away!

The new flow was a good one. The windmill was replaced and we were saved. We owed Jim five hundred dollars after believing that all had been paid for but he kindly let us pay him in installments.

Mother returned in June on her way back east and was pleased and impressed with the complete change from almost bare desert to a new, small comfortable home with definite signs of green grass, small shrubs and trees. Also there were two puppies in the pen around the dog house and two kittens who ate out of the same dish with the pups.

I think that in the ten days or so she spent with us she began to love New Mexico and realized that Bill and I were going to have a happy life together.

For anyone reading this who has not read BILL MARTIN, AMERICAN now reprinted by the Vantage Press, New York, N.Y.

Bill was born in St. Croix, Vaud, Switzerland in 1895. One of nine children he had to work hard from early childhood. Like most Swiss children he spent a year each with a family in the German then with Italian speaking parts of that country. In this way he learned to speak two other languages besides his native French. However he had little formal education, (probably not more than through what, in the United States would be the sixth or seventh grade.)

He earned enough money by age fifteen to buy steerage passage to North Canada in 1911 where he worked on some big ranches. There he grew up very rapidly and learned an enormous amount of all the practical things in life. He had several unusual and exciting experiences including spending one winter alone in the frozen north caring for hundreds of cattle and a "freighting" trip with his boss to trade for furs with the Indians in North Saskatchewan.

Encounters with the fine Northwest Mounted Police inspired him to go into the "law and order" field. He went to New York City and studied and worked under the famous Valentine of the then fine New York Police.

As, what might be called a counter-spy, he crossed the Atlantic several times as valet to a German spy during World War I before the U.S. entered the war. He got his evidence and the German was turned over to the French for conviction.

Until the early twenties he worked as an investigator for the New York police. In the meantime he had married a French Canadian girl whose health started to fail after the birth of twin girls who died at birth.

In 1923 he brought his ailing wife to the sunny New Mexico climate in Santa Fe. Here he worked at various jobs until he became well enough known so that a few friends realized that he was a fine detective and investigator. Within a year he was being called on to investigate robberies, hold-ups and murders.

He was soon invited to join the Santa Fe Volunteer Fire Department which was then in its infancy, as their fire marshal. Not long thereafter he helped form the first New Mexico State Police and later became its special investigator.

During the years of 1924 to 1936 he investigated one hundred and seventy four serious criminal cases and in close cooperation with two district attorneys, John J. Kenney and David Chavez laid the foundation for about one hundred and sixty five convictions! These took him all over the state—sometimes beyond its borders. He tracked down criminals on horseback, on foot (sometimes in an old Model A Ford) thru the mountains and over dry semi-deserts. Because of his increasing success and "fame" he was called on to work at many cases for the F.B.I., and its forerunner. (There were no F.B.I. men or even Postal Inspectors in New Mexico until the mid or late thirties!)

He resigned from the State Police along with six or seven

other officers in late 1936 because of political interference with his duties.

In World War II he was a troop Transport Commander, (also, secretly an intelligence officer) crossing the Pacific twelve times. Later, as his health began to fail, he was put in charge of P.O.W. camps—one at Holabird, Md., the other at Fort Monroe, Va. He was invalided home before the end of the war.

For the rest it will be told in the upcoming pages.

After mother had left to spend the summer in England near the Furness family where she could see her two little granddaughters often, Bill and I really began "living." Most of the initial building was completed and we concentrated on planting. A small vegetable garden was started, fruit trees set out, as well as silver lace vine, and Rose of Castille shrubs. These shoots were given us by Carl and Lois Gilbert who said that the original shoots they had planted years earlier had come from Archbishop Lamy's garden!

There were no homes within sight of us at that time, and the wide open spaces around us, with three mountain ranges—the Sangre de Cristos to the north, the Jemez to the west, and the Sandias to the south—appeared very close in the perfectly clear air. Because of our relative isolation there was plenty of wildlife of all kinds on the place. Coveys of quail were on the front lawn morning and evening as well as up around the pool. Before Bill and I were married he used to enjoy hunting doves and quail as well as larger game. However, after the small birds became our friends he never shot another. There were dozens of cottontails and some jackrabbits which the pups loved to chase but never caught. Jerry, the calico cat, occasionally caught one, as well as numerous mice, after she was grown, and amazingly she would bring her prey home and share her feast with the half-grown collies.

Other animals not so welcome were skunks, porcupines, and rattlesnakes. Fortunately, most of our domestic animals had a great respect for such creatures, and over the ensuing years we only had one Great Dane who got too nosey with a porcupine, to his regret! When skunks came very close to any of the buildings, both cats and dogs would sit, disgusted, watching them wander about unconcernedly but never tangling with them.

As far as rattlesnakes went, I, personally, never got over my fear and hatred of them. That summer on Los Piñones I met my first one. Bill was off on a private investigative case. I was cleaning the living room. The doors and windows were open and the two collie pups were romping on the front lawn. Suddenly I heard sharp, alarmed barking. Looking out the large front window I saw Susan and Dusty slowly stalking about in a circle. At the same time I heard a distinct buzzing sound and spotted something in the middle of the circle. I had never seen or heard a rattlesnake in my life but I knew what it was.

Grabbing Bill's six-shooter from the hall table where it always rested when I was alone on the place, I went to the steps of the front porch, calling to the pups. Thank heavens they came to me immediately and I shut them in the house. Then, trembling, I stepped to the edge of the lawn and took a good look at the still coiled snake about thirty feet from me. I raised my shaking hand holding the loaded revolver, took aim, and fired. The evil little head dropped. I stood rooted to the spot, watching the thing coiling and uncoiling in its death throes.

Not until some ten minutes after my victim lay still did I dare approach him close enough so that I could see that I'd shot his head off! Then I relaxed and looked about me. In a small piñon tree I saw the two half-grown kittens, Tom and Jerry, looking down very solemnly with their round eyes riveted on the dead reptile. Quickly I returned to the house, laid the gun on the table, gathered the two excited pups in my arms, and returned them to their pen. Then I heaved a sigh of relief, remembering that Bill was due home in a couple of hours.

When he arrived I silently led him by the hand to the front lawn. He picked up the five-foot snake and counted the twelve rattles on the tail. After he had disposed of the carcass he opened the revolver, saw that only one shot had been fired, and looked at me in amazement.

"One shot from thirty feet away and you hit that tiny

head! And you told me you had never fired a gun except a rifle in a shooting gallery!"

I replied, "That's true. I was so scared and my hand was waving around so it's a wonder I didn't hit one of the kittens in the bush. It was just fool luck and I don't want to ever touch another gun!"

"Oh, yes, you will. We'll set up some tin cans in the arroyo and you can have lots of practice, although I doubt that you need it. By the way, a better weapon for a snake is a good old garden hoe. Remember that next time."

I nodded and secretly hoped there would be no next time.

The following day Bill went to town and told everyone he met (and he knew almost everyone in town) what an "Annie Oakley" his bride was! The result of that was that later in the summer a lone woman neighbor, about a mile away from us, phoned me that she had a rattlesnake in her yard —would I please come and kill it? Again Bill was not at home, so I went over and dispatched my second snake—with a hoe!

Bill had bought a lovely little singlefoot horse named Caesar for me who joined Speck in the pasture and we rode over the countryside very often. The two collies joyfully followed us on these jaunts and, amazingly, the cat Jerry did, too! Women's Lib! She was always with us. She caught all the mice. Tom, her boyfriend, was too lazy and was good for nothing but tomcatting about the countryside, getting into fights, and then coming home to have Jerry lick his wounds! One day he roamed too far and never returned. We weren't too sad about it as he was good for little except howling and keeping us awake.

Bill was an avid trout fisherman and started to teach me to cast a line that first summer. One day in early fall we went up into the beautiful Chama country where Bill had some business. We went fishing on the Brazos River the next day. Unlike the Rio Grande, this delightful stream is heavily wooded along its banks. Bill, as usual, was well ahead of me, round several bends in the river, constantly on the move. At one point he thought he had better backtrack and see how I was getting along.

Reaching a small clearing he saw my creel on the bank

126

but no other sign. He called and I answered from the branch of a tree over his head.

"What in the devil are you doing up there?"

"I'm retrieving my fish."

With arms akimbo, he watched while I untangled a flopping ten-inch trout from the branches. When I climbed down with a mess of tangled line and the well hooked fish, I proudly held it out to him saying, "Look, the first trout I ever caught that was big enough so I didn't have to throw it back!"

"Well, he's a beauty but why did you have to find him in a tree?"

"You see, you've taught me how to cast a fly and make it land somewhere near the spot I want it to—but we never fished before where there wasn't plenty of room behind me. When I felt the strike I just yanked!"

Upshot—for the next several weeks Bill would brag to the town's folk that his citified wife could not only shoot snakes in the head with a thirty-six revolver but now knew how to find fish in the trees!

* * * * *

By autumn, dear Caroline Dozier returned to us. She had discovered why the woman who "stole" her from us offered her so much more pay. Caroline said it wasn't worth it. Could she please come back to the Martins who treated her like one of the family. We welcomed her with open arms. Since mother was about to come through Santa Fe for a few weeks' visit with us, this was especially timely. There wasn't enough room in our two-bedroom house for four of us so Caroline would have to stay in town for a while longer but she came in almost daily and was of great help.

After mother's arrival I showed her tentative plans I'd drawn for an addition to our house which would be an independent apartment—a real home base for mother in between her travels. In the fourteen years since she had left Oshkosh for good she had never had a home of her own with her own things permanently settled in one place. Now Bill had suggested and I heartily agreed that if she could learn to like New Mexico this might be a logical place for her pied-a-terre, part way between her winters in California, her friends and relatives in the Midwest, and New York. Most summers she would undoubtedly spend near **Phyllis and** family in England. However, none of us could see **her being** able to stand that climate for the balance of the year.

Mother, whose generosity had made it possible for us to build much more of a home than we otherwise could have done, was definitely pleased that the suggestion had originally come from Bill. She studied my plans and began to picture what it would be like to have a home of her own to come back to whenever she wanted and where she could leave her nice possessions without periodically storing or moving them. She also could see how this relatively barren, desolate countryside was beginning to sprout greenery, blossoms, etc., which would enhance the natural beauty of sunny blue skies and handsome mountains. It didn't take her long to agree. She sketched into my plans inside details as she would like them. We were to build the apartment and pay for it as it was to be an integral part of our house, and she would pay for Caroline and her share of running expenses.

As soon as she had left for California we started in with the fun of building the new living room, bedroom, bath, and kitchenette, plus an attractive patio. Little did any of us know to what good use this addition would be put in the future thirty-odd years.

During the late fall Bill and I took off occasionally for mountain hunting and fishing trips. We had an old beat-up Ford station wagon in which we camped. We always took along a pick, shovel, and burlap bags. Then, while up in the tall trees, we dug up, with permits from the Forest Service, small fir, spruce, and pine trees which we carefully planted about our home. Most of these survived—to such an extent that later we had to thin some of them out as they began to block our views of the mountains. Some were dug up and given to neighbors, and for a number of years we cut our own Christmas trees, also many varieties of evergreen branches from our own front yard. I still gather my own greens at holiday time thirty-five years later.

One rather amusing but also sad incident arose a few years later in regard to trees. In the early years after mother was well established periodically in her apartment, she asked Bill if he could find a long needle pine in the mountains, to be planted in her patio against the fireplace chimney. These were notoriously hard to transplant from the rocky soil in the higher elevations. However, he said he'd try. He found one just the right shape and size and duly put it in the patio. Then we all prayed that it would live and thrive. It did, and made a nice green design against the light adobe-colored wall. It did so well, in fact, that one day a few years later we discovered that its rapidly growing feathery branches extended so far to each side that it had blocked all sunlight from the French doors on one side and the French windows on the other. The attractive apartment living room was so darkened that mother needed artificial light in the daytime. We did try to cut and thin out some of the offending branches but the end result was a pathetic skeleton, and the tree had to come out.

A year after we had built mother's apartment we built a battery chicken house as well as a small rental house which was on part of our property within the city limits of Santa Fe. Bill ordered fifty to a hundred baby chicks and raised them in wire cages which we built ourselves. There were also eight cages for laying hens. It seemed rather inhuman but that is the way almost all poultry is raised these days, and with a warm "year-around home" and highpower feeding he produced hundreds of excellent broilers which more than paid for themselves and gave Bill plenty to do when he was not off on an investigation.

He was given a handsome young horse to train at one point and the spooky animal gave him a bad fall which resulted in a dislocated shoulder. Our dear friend, Dr. Albert Lathrop, came out to reduce it. Because of Bill's powerful musculature, Al was unable to do so without some relaxation—so I had my first human patient in several years. (Living on a ranch, I had, of necessity, given shots, sewed up barbed-wire tears on the dogs, etc.)

In this instance I administered my first anesthetic since I had been on the "delivery" district in Chicago in 1932. Not much fun to work on your own husband but the ether put Bill to sleep, Al got the shoulder back in place, and instead of my patient awakening violently sick, he came to roaring drunk. It was a beautiful happy drunkenness which had the doctor, Caroline, and me helpless with laughter.

Little did I know that in a few years' time I would be putting all the surgical cases in Santa Fe to sleep—to be exact, three thousand of them!

CHAPTER IX. WAR CLOUDS

(MOLLY)

Mother was in England, as usual, in August 1939 when World War II broke out. Remarkable, sensible woman that she was, she calmly waited until the hordes of Americans and others who stormed the consulates and the Embassy for passage home had thinned out. Then she obtained passage for New York on the S.S. Harding. She was lucky to get a cabin with only two roommates. The ship was vastly overcrowded, with passengers berthed in the common rooms, companionways, etc. They were at sea for about two or three days before the startled passengers were aware of the fact that they weren't headed west for the United States but were approaching Bordeaux!

There they picked up many-tongued refugees (mostly American citizens living abroad) who frantically dashed aboard the already over-crowded ship. No bombs had yet begun to fall but there were plenty of submarines doing their dirty work and all the sundry just hoped the Germans would respect the neutrality of the well lighted American ship.

Mother encountered many fellow shipmates who anxiously tried to count the numbers aboard and then the number of lifeboat seats, rafts, and life belts. Mary Radford simply retired to any available place to sit and read her ever-present books, knowing how futile it was to hope to be saved if the ship were to be torpedoed.

Three days later they discovered that the Harding was zigzagging about the Irish Sea. The skipper had received an S. O. S. from a sinking Danish ship and we was trying to find survivors in the cold, foggy waters.

About three AM the ship's engines stopped. Mother looked out of her porthole and saw three ghostlike lifeboats which approached the ship's Jacob's ladder. She watched the soaked, exhausted sailors climb slowly aboard—right past her port. There were thirty-three men who had survived.

Sometime after daylight she and others learned that these men were French; they had been aboard a tanker, the Emil Miguet, which had *no* radio. They had sent no message and felt that the good Lord had sent the Harding across their path while she was looking for another sinking ship. Grim as the situation seemed to all, the rescuing of these men put a good deal of spirit into the whole company. For a few days she was almost a happy ship in spite of the mass of humanity aboard.

Then the hurricane struck, just off the Grand Banks, about six hundred miles from home port. The ship's captain had, of course, had warning and had ordered everyone to his or her bunk in mid-evening. People being people, lots of them disregarded orders and stayed up to "watch the fun." Mary Radford went to her bunk and went to sleep. When the ship heeled over to such a degree that it seemed about to overturn, passengers, furniture, dishes, life rafts, etc., went flying or sliding or crashing.

Mother awoke in the bunk across the cabin, with her arm in a bureau drawer. She had flown through the air over the middle bunk, and because she had been asleep and relaxed she suffered not one bruise. Many others ended up with broken arms, legs, backs, and other severe wounds. The night chef in the galley had been very badly burned and numerous others were severely injured by flying dishes, glass, and other debris. Mother's table steward, a nice young man from our home state of Wisconsin, had unwisely sought a breath of fresh air at the wrong moment and had been washed overboard—the only fatality.

In Santa Fe, almost three thousand miles away, Bill Martin was listening to the morning news on the radio. I awoke hearing the words, "President Harding," and dashed into the living room to hear the account of what had happened to the ship I knew mother was on. Coast Guard cutters were dashing to the scene but the extent of the damage was not known to the announcer.

I went to the phone to send a wire to Aunt Hat in New

York, hoping that she or Uncle Don might be able to get some information. The man at our telegraph office said, as soon as I gave my name,

"Just a minute, Mrs. Martin, There's a radiogram just came in for you. It says, 'Well, safe' "! So within minutes of hearing of the disaster, I knew that my mother was all right. That was not just thanks to fairly rapid communication of those days but more to my indomitable mother's wits. Within five minutes of the great crash mother had scribbled my name, address, and the message, and handed it to a passing steward who had somehow, in the great confusion, delivered it to the radio shack before all private messages were disallowed. Thus I was saved the agonizing waiting to hear good or bad news. This is how World War II first reached us personally in the Wild West.

Addendum—After mother came home she told us of two incidents. One woman aboard whom mother got to know slightly had never appeared in the lounges, dining rooms, or on deck without being completely groomed as if for a party. From the first day at sea she wore hat, coat, jewelry, scarf, high-heeled shoes, and clutched a beautiful bulging purse. The day after the hurricane struck, this woman appeared on deck in a wrinkled house dress, bobby socks, tennis shoes, and no purse. Her hair was streaming down her back and she wasn't even carrying gloves! She was relaxed and smiling, saying, "Nothing in the world can happen after this!"

The other item was that on the last day before landing in New York, the ship's captain told mother that if it hadn't been for the French skipper of the torpedoed Emil Miguet who had been on the bridge with him the night the hurricane struck, they probably would not be alive to tell the tale. The tanker's skipper with unusual knowledge of the sea had saved the Harding from capsizing!

* * * * *

At this point, before I get more involved with my own story, it seems to me a good time to write a chapter about that amazing person, Mary Radford, my mother. Often, during the second half of my life when I have tried a bit of writing, I have thought and even started a book about mother. I proba-

bly will never be able to manage it; therefore, I want to incorporate the highlights of her life now. Unlike many mothers and daughters, our experiences have been inextricably entwined during the greater part of my existence.

CHAPTER X. MARY

(MOLLY)

From the time that our home was broken up in 1923 and mother went East to earn her own way at age 49, she never really looked back. Instead of sinking into any kind of self-pity and/or any recriminations, she went rapidly forward. Both in her job and in her free time she read omniverously on every conceivable subject. She wrote thousands of letters, keeping in close touch with relatives and friends, old and new. In spite of her severe asthma, which literally incapacitated her at times, she never failed, wherever she was, to see and talk with anyone she knew, and liked to renew in person the contacts she valued.

As a result, she not only deepened her friendships but held them all of her life.

Dora Drane, whom she had known since they were eight years old, had a greatly varied life, a good deal of it tragic. For over sixty-five years mother never lost track of her. She would go to see her in Chicago or New York, or invite Dora to lunch or dine with her *every* time they were in the same city. Dora, before and during her troubles, was a deep reader and thinker. She delved into philosophy and mysticism and became quite a dedicated student and practitioner in psychic phenomena.

For a good many years mother followed her friend in these pursuits. Both mother's sister, my Aunt Harriet, and Cousin Catherine did the same. Without any professional "medium" they and numerous other interested friends amassed quantities of spiritual material. Between mother, Aunt Harriet, and Dora they published privately several books on the subject. Two of these were THE INEVITABLE VOYAGE and THE MESSAGES OF PLATONIUS. It is interesting to note that books on the subject periodically come out in great numbers. Many are scoffed at, some considered fraudulent, but almost each generation shows a strong interest in metaphysical things. Just in the past few months (1972) TIME Magazine devoted a cover story to the subject. Personally, I have carried within me a deep and abiding belief in life after death because of this influence.

Hazel Winkler from Milwaukee was a close friend of mother's from the time they were teenagers. They didn't see each other for years after Hazel and her family moved to California. However, when mother started going out there winters in the early 1930s, she looked up her old friend. From then on they and our families have kept an abiding, close friendship. Hazel in her later years became almost blind. (I now have the same "Macular degeneration.") When mother's later strokes produced a "central blindness," she asked me to write Hazel, "I'm glad this has happened to me, for now I understand what you have been going through for years."

At one point when mother was visiting the Winklers, mother mentioned how she had always regretted the fact that she had never been to college and didn't have the education so many others had. Pat, Hazel's husband, said, "Mary Radford, you are the best educated person I have ever known, man or woman."

After she had inherited and been given enough money from Catherine and by Uncle, mother studied finance so thoroughly that her Chicago bankers often bowed to her decisions when it came to reinvesting some of her funds.

Her interest in theater and music increased through every year of her adult life. She never missed the best plays whenever she was in a big city, particularly New York and London, and "took in" everything from Greek drama through Shakespeare, Noel Coward, Beatrice Lillie, and T.S. Eliot. She not only enjoyed but remembered practically every performance she saw. (I doubt that, if she had lived into the '60s, she would have attended many theatres!) Even when she was invalided she read all the reviews or had them read to her.

From her early days in suffrage work she took a keen interest in politics and never voted for candidates until she had read up on them thoroughly and/or discussed them with men or women whose opinions she respected.

She should have been a writer—she always said she had printer's ink in her blood. If she had been born a bit later, I like to think that she would have been a well known journalist such as Marguerite Higgins. F.P.A., H.L. Mencken, B.L.T., Alexander Woolcott, Dorothy Thompson, and others of their times were among her favorites in the newspaper world.

Apropos of her fascination with the printed word—in 1925 when she took Phyllis and her roommate to Europe on her meagre savings she was necessarily engrossed much of the time with the cost of fares, hotels, bus trips, etc. One day, I believe it was in Carcassonne, the girls had gone on a hike over the lovely countryside in beautiful sunshine. Mother settled herself under a tree where she could look off to a gorgeous view. When the girls returned a couple of hours later, Phyllis saw her mother busily writing in a notebook.

The twenty-four-year-old approached her fifty-year-old parent, saying in disgust,

"Mother, you just can't be doing your accounts at this time in this lovely place!"

Mary Radford looked up at her daughter, said nothing, but handed the girl the notebook. Phyllis, dumbfounded, saw that her mother had written a couple of pages of poetry.

Words and common sense were integral parts of mother's life. When I was about nine years old, mother heard me call my playmate, Bob, a "darned fool." (What would a child that age say instead today?) Mother took me aside and said,

"There are a lot worse and stronger expressions you'll learn some day. The important thing to keep in mind is to use them at the right place and the right time. If you use a strong swearword when you are slightly angry, what will you have left to say when you are really mad or terribly hurt?"

Later in life, when we were discussing sex, chastity, etc., mother's comment on promiscuity was, "The best and most fundamental reason for a girl to reserve her 'favors' is that the man she may come to love and marry would like to be certain that their children are his!"

During World War II we were talking about some young friends who were marrying in great haste before the boys were shipped overseas. When I made some unthinking remark about marrying in haste and repenting at leisure, mother said,

"In some cases it is probably very foolish, but—a young man going off to war, whether he knows it or not, has a compelling urge to be sure that his life will continue on earth."

On the subject of death her views were very pragmatic. In her later years she was often very ill—enough to worry me to distraction, particularly when soon after recovery she'd be merrily on her way across the Atlantic. More than once she had been known to shock her room stewardess by saying on the first day out,

"Now don't forget. If I happen to die before we reach port, tell the captain just to shove the old carcass overboard—it's really nothing but an old overcoat."

The above and many more incidents are vividly with me as I near my seventies. Two of her favorite quotes were:

"When I was young, my shoes were red,
  I kicked my heels right over my head.

"Then I grew up and my shoes were white
  I danced the stars clear out of the night.

"Now I am old and my shoes are black
  I walk to the corner—and then I walk back.

"You ask how I know my youth is now spent?
  My get-up-and-go has got up and went.
  But still I can grin when I think where
    It's been!"

CHAPTER XI. REFUGEES

(MOLLY)

Mother's memorable trip on the Harding in the fall of 1939 was her last transatlantic crossing for eight years. Little did we know how long it would be before she could go again. However, at that point we also didn't know how soon it would be before most of our family would be reunited.

During the "cold war" that winter we naturally followed the news closely. By early spring we were listening to the radio many more times a day. Mother and I both wrote Phyl frequently, begging her to come to this country or at least bring the children, Diana and Elizabeth (Beebi) to us.

When France fell and the tremendous Dunkirk evacuation had been completed, Phyllis cabled us that she was bringing the little girls to Santa Fe as soon as they could get some kind of passage. Fortunately, the small rental house Bill and I had built was to be vacated by the young couple living in it as the man had joined the service by then. That meant that we had room for seven of us—including dear Caroline Dozier. We knew we would need her help to cope with so many persons as well as the never-ending ranch jobs.

By June, mother went to New York, had a short visit with the Dallas family, and met the "refugees." When the Santa Fe Chief brought the four of them to us it was not only a joyful reunion but also a first meeting for Bill and the Furnesses and for me and my two nieces aged four and a half and seven. We got them all settled, the children occupying mother's apartment living room as their dormitory, and Bill and I moved into the rental house.

It was a confused few days. Beebie was extremely shy with us at first. Of course she and Diana knew their "Goggie" well, so the transition for them was not too difficult. However, Phyllis was too preoccupied to focus on much beside the fact that her children were safe. Unbeknownst to us she had already made plans to return to George (strictly against British and American regulations). The latter who had been a "territorial" (equivalent to our national guard) was naturally by then in the regular British army.

The rest of us were appalled at the thought of her returning under the bombs, and Phyl, between leaving her children—for how long?—and rejoining her husband—under what was to come?—had more than "enough on her plate."

Fortunately, Diana and Beebi were too young to realize all the implications, and when their mother left were soon absorbed in a game they were playing. It didn't take long for them to revel in the new freedom of country American living. (They had been brought up with a governess and/or "nanny.") The sunshine, the dogs (two collies and a Great Dane by then), a cat, Jerry, chickens, two horses, and a swimming pool were all theirs to enjoy.

Bill soon bought them a gentle pony, built them a sandbox and swing, and fell in love with both of them. He had always wanted children, which I had been unable to give him, and adored all youngsters. That meant that I had to restrain myself a bit in order to maintain a minimum of discipline. Diana was an outgoing enthusiastic half-angel and half-devil and beautiful. Beebi, once over her shyness, was quieter and had an engaging, unruffable disposition. That summer was heaven for us all except for the nagging worry over Phyllis and George. The former had arrived in Liverpool, safely, thank God, but we didn't know until much later that she was greeted there by one of the war's worst bombing raids!

In midsummer, Susan, the white collie, had nine puppies, sired by a fine tricolor collie of our neighbors, Dr. and Mrs. Corbusier, who were by then close friends. Barbara Stevenson, their second daughter, had moved with her family to Santa Fe and they were building a large home not too far away which "my" children and I watched going up. Bambi and Dondi Stevenson the Lathrop girls and other children appeared often to swim, and I found myself back in the happy business of teaching my favorite sport once again.

There were other English "refugees" by then in Santa Fe. (In all there were fourteen of them in our relatively small town.) The John Meems who lived about a mile up the road from us had "adopted" four young daughters of a doctor in Bath. These girls ranged in age from twelve to six. Faith and John's own child, Nancy, was only two years old.

By autumn the Meems had decided to start a nursery school in their large, beautiful home, and the youngsters from age two to five or six, including our Beebi, had a wonderful preschool experience there under the tutelage of a remarkable woman, Miss Gebhardt. The older Mathew girls and Diana were entered in the fine Brownmoore School which was then operating in the famous Bishop's Lodge north of town during the academic year. (It was and still is a delightful "Dude Ranch Hotel" during the summer.) Faith and I took turns driving the five girls to and from the school bus in Santa Fe, so we all got quite well acquainted. With swimming, picnics, parties, as well as school together, this maintained a bit of "Old England" in our girls which I'm afraid didn't counteract entirely the effects of the free Wild-West kind of living which was turning all of them into regular little Americans. Diana, especially, did her best to lose her British accent.

However, it turned out happily that the Furness family were only separated for almost a year and a half. In the fall of 1941 George was ordered to Washington, D. C. on the "Lend Lease" deal. He came over on a troop ship and Phyllis wangled her passage via Lisbon. She went to Washington first to find a home for her reunited family and then dashed West to recover her "lost" children.

What a reunion that was! Beebi had almost forgotten England and her mother—she had chicken-pox and looked a mess, too! But soon the long months of separation were forgotten and mother and daughters returned East. Happy as we were to see them reunited, Bill and I were sunk for awhile after losing "our" beloved little girls who had had our Los Piñones ringing with joy and laughter for some sixteen months.

The four Mathews girls remained with the Meems for five years. Faith and John, as well as Faith's wonderful Aunt

Elinor who had taken in two British boys, kept in touch in the ensuing years. Just last summer, 1972, Judie, Bridget, Gillian, and Elizabeth Mathews left four husbands, sixteen children, and England and traveled to Santa Fe to visit their war-time parents. "Aunt Faith and Uncle John," for a couple of weeks. Faith, John, and grown-up Nancy with her husband John and children gave a wonderful party, inviting everyone who had had any close contact with their English children during the war years thirty years before. I'm sorry that our two, Diana and Elizabeth, couldn't have been present.

To go back to 1941. Bill and I didn't have too long a time to regret losing our two, as directly after Pearl Harbor Bill volunteered to serve his adopted country in whatever capacity it could use him. As our local physicians went off to war, I fell heir to numerous clinics, first aid teaching, and other medically related jobs.

(Bill was called up in mid-1942—and his story is to be found in my book, BILL MARTIN, AMERICAN which was in print from 1959-1961 and is now reprinted, by the Vantage Press, New York.)

CHAPTER XII.
RETURN TO MEDICINE

For the Third Time 1942-1948

(MOLLY)

One of my more interesting, if exasperating, jobs in the early years of the war was to conduct a "well baby" clinic in the outlying small towns and villages of Santa Fe County. This was funded under a new federal program, and the idea behind it was a good one. Such clinics have done a world of good over the years, especially in large urban areas, where the poor may take their infants regularly to see a doctor for a routine check. If some incipient trouble appeared the mother was referred to a doctor for early treatment. The program was primarily preventive.

Mary Jane Carter, a very superior public health nurse, and I were assigned to set up and carry out such clinics in about eight or ten villages spread over a good-sized area. Mary Jane ingeniously devised a set of equipment which could be condensed into a relatively small package which would fit into the trunk of her car. This included linens, tongue depressors, scales, a tape measure, antiseptics, etc. That wonderful girl wisely included whatever evaporated milk, cod liver oil, and occasionally a few of the early sulfa drugs she had scrounged from kindhearted souls. She knew Santa Fe County and something of its Mexican-American population from previous work over the countryside.

Each week we went to a different community where the mothers of small babies had been, presumably, told to meet us at the local school house at a given time. It had been some years since I had done any kind of medical work with patients and during my years of ranch life I had forgotten much. However, I had been assured that my only job would be to examine well babies and give general advice. So we started out.

It didn't matter which community we visited; practically all the families were very poor. The depression of the thirties still hung on and few of the men had jobs. The one saving grace was that most lived on some sort of tiny farm and grew a modest amount of food to keep body and soul together. Even so, severe drought in that always semi-desert land had reduced their food supplies, particularly for farm animals. Therefore many families didn't even have a cow, pig, or chickens.

To add to the problems, the few doctors who had practiced in those remote sections had left to join the military services. Even some of those in somewhat larger towns couldn't make a living and had left for more populated regions. Few families had cars in order to go farther afield to reach a doctor when they knew where one was. Sometimes a visiting county nurse might arrive at one or another community a few times a year.

One of the first clinics Mary Jane and I held was, as always, in the school house. There the local women had cleaned it up, set up a table for us, and had several mothers and infants awaiting us. The mothers regarded it as a social occasion and were happily chatting, glad of a chance to sit down and an excuse not to be doing stoop labor in the poor bean, chili, or corn fields. In those days few of those young mothers spoke English and I was embarrassed not to be able to speak more than a very few words of Spanish. However, Mary Jane could do very well with the language and there were often one or two Spanish-Americans who had some English. Things went quite well for us but it troubled me that a number of our mothers had brought older children with a variety of ailments. They also begged us to come to their homes to see an ailing uncle or grandmother, etc. Here was a nurse and a doctor, and of course their business was to take care of the sick and injured!

Our instructions were never to go into a private home and to tell the people to take the ailing ones of any age to the nearest doctor in regular practice. We were there to examine *only well* babies and to advise the parents on matters of nutrition, cleanliness, etc.

One of my early young patients was not "sick," he was simply starving. At six months of age he weighed *six* pounds. The young mother was about five months pregnant and had no breast milk. (In some cases we saw children two or three years old still suckling.) We asked the mother what she fed the baby.

She replied, "Oh, I give him a whole bottle of milk every time he cries." We asked her to demonstrate what she put in the bottle, not believing her story. Thereupon she took a bottle and a can of evaporated milk Mary Jane produced, carefully measured two ounces of the milk into the bottle, and filled it up with water, saying, "That's what the nurse told me to do when he was born—except not much water. When he grows older, he need more, so I give him bigger bottle."

Appalled, we told her the obvious.

"I know, but there's not enough milk for the others. He's small, don't need so much. Anyway, he no sick, no even cry now."

Poor little scrap of humanity—he didn't have the strength to cry. What was amazing was that he was alive. We brought out some of our small supply of milk and demonstrated how much to give the child. (The next year we saw the same mother with her next child and she was doing just as she had done with the first one we had seen. We didn't have the heart to ask if the former one was on earth!)

Advice on proper nutrition in a case like that?! I was learning rapidly. These people "made do" with what was available. Most of them subsisted on beans and chili. I learned that almost all of them started their babies on these two items very early when there was no milk. I had not lived long enough in New Mexico to learn to eat chili anywhere nearly as hot as the natives did. I was developing a real taste for it—but for small babies? Mary Jane assured me that it was amazing how they could tolerate it, and, as I knew, it was a pretty good source of vitamin C.

Beans, of course, are not only nourishing but a reasonably good source of protein. Mary Jane, my guide and mentor, found a recipe of sorts which involved making a puree of beans, causing them to be more digestible for small fry. This information we passed on, although we never knew how many mothers really bothered to follow it.

Vitamin D, another essential, especially for the young, proved a problem in more ways than one. In this extremely sunny country one would think that the children could and would absorb enough of that vitamin through the skin. However, the average Spanish-American hereabouts, at least in those days, seemed to fear the sun and bundled their youngsters up in any clothes available, summer and winter.

It appeared to me that numerous mothers had heard of cod liver oil, probably from some nurse or doctor before us. The lanaguage barrier had possibly been responsible for the mothers' confusion. In any case, to our great distress we found that many mothers gave their infants *Castor Oil,* sometimes nightly! This, of course, produced the logical results and the next day the babe would get a dose of "Baby Percy," a patent medicine which I believe contains bismuth and is supposed to cure diarrhea.

Now, diarrhea is one thing Mexican kids don't need to have given to them. The Good Lord knows that poorly built privies, swarming with flies which contaminate even fresh food, combined with general dirty conditions in the household, produced enough infectious diarrhea to cause an unbelievable infant death toll in those days. And, of course, starvation simply aggravates the run-off and dehydration, and vice versa.

Aside from our many nutritional problems with our so-called "well babies," other worries plagued us. In spite of stern rules and regulations our consciences would not let us refuse aid to the sick or injured—older children with "nits" in the hair, skinned knees, broken arms, etc. We gave what first aid we could and directed them to the nearest practicing physician, even though we were forbidden to look at them or touch them.

We even went further in breaking the rules! On one occasion we were persuaded to go into a home where we found a twelve-year-old boy with an obvious case of typhoid fever. We didn't know how long he had been ill. About all we could do was to report the case to our superiors—after all, it was a public health matter!

Another time we went into a home and found the grandfather and a granddaughter in bed in one tiny stuffy room. Even my unpractised ears could diagnose a fulminating pneumonia in each chest. We left the house, leaving behind the few sulfa tablets we had, with instructions (there was no penicillin in those days) to get the patients in to Santa Fe as quickly as possible. I heard later from wonderful old Dr. Ward that the grandfather had been carried into his office the next day in a dying state. The good doctor got him into the hospital across the street before he died. The patient had been brought about twenty miles on a pile of straw in a horse-drawn wagon—nobody in that village had a car! We never knew what happened to the little girl but someone said she had survived, whether due to the sulfa or her youthful stamina.

Dear May Jane, who is still one of my cherished friends, continued to try to do her best for these people for a time after I was called to do other work. She reported that the second year conditions were somewhat better as more men got jobs in various plants essential to the war effort.

* * * * *

My new job came as a surprise. Bill was shipped to the Pacific in early 1943. Being quite convinced that I shouldn't see him until the end of the war, I had an urge to get into it myself. I applied to the Waves, passed my physical, and was about to rent our home when I received a delegation. Several of my good doctor friends came with the word that Dr. Williams, the general practitioner in town who gave all the anesthetics at St. Vincent hospital (the only hospital in town) had had a slight heart attack.

Dr. Fiske, Dr. Ward, and a few others who did surgery said that I must not leave but should prepare myself for taking over all the anesthesia in town! In 1941, before we got into the war, I had gone back to Billings hospital to take a few weeks as a substitute anesthetist. I had done this at the urging of my medical friends who at the time felt that the day would come when Dr. Williams would not be able to carry the load. However, in the intervening period all had

147

seemed to be going well, so I had more or less dismissed it from my mind.

Now Dr. Williams needed me and I dropped everything else and went to the operating room daily and "understudied," as it were, as an assistant anesthetist. It was a good thing I got that early a start as a couple of months later Dr. William's next heart attack killed him. I was scared to death at the responsibility which now landed on my shoulders.

My blessed surgeon friends were patient with me, advised and encouraged me, and often praised my work even before I deserved any. Naturally I had been reading and continued to read all the books on anesthesia I could get. (The science and practice of that branch of medicine was nowhere nearly so complicated as it is today.) One thing which was a godsend to me was that I not only had been "put to sleep" myself more than once but had suffered serious illness in my life. This, I firmly believe, is an enormous help in understanding the patient's frame of mind, his fears of the unknown, as well as his apprehensions about many little details. This, to me, is the "art" of medicine, and I did my best to be as concerned about my patients' state of mind as I was about the technical side of anesthetizing a person.

From the beginning, I always visited my patient the night before surgery, unless it was an emergency. Aside from reading his medical history on the chart, I would get as much as possible of his experience from his own lips. I took pains to tell him each step which was to be taken before he went to sleep so that he would know exactly what to expect. Then I would urge him to ask any questions he wished.

After surgery (there were no recovery rooms, no orderlies, and not enough nurses), I always returned with my patients to their rooms and talked with members of the family. I could not stay with the patients until they awoke, in most cases, as I had to set up for the next case in a very few minutes. With the shortages of floor nurses, and a few incompetent or indifferent ones, I always worried about the ones coming out of the anesthetic. Whenever there was a minute to spare I would check on previous patients. I was a devil with some careless nurses who left a helpless patient in the wrong position or were negligent in some other way. More than once I got into trouble with my criticism or complaints. However, I didn't care—my only concern was with the well-being and care of the patient, and the surgeons always backed me up. There were one or two occasions when I suspect I might have been fired or thrown off the staff. Thanks to my surgeon friends I wasn't, and I suppose the authorities couldn't do it anyway as there was only one other doctor in town who occasionally poured ether when there were two cases at once or I was sick or unavailable. (I was "unavailable" on a few occasions in those five years when Bill came out of the Pacific and I would dash to San Francisco for a couple of days between his many crossings to the South Seas.)

I seldom failed to visit my patients at least once or twice in the days following their surgery and I believed they appreciated it. I, in turn, learned much for my own information, as usually they were as open and frank about their experiences as I had been with them about what to expect beforehand.

It is difficult to remember details of those strenuous times after almost twenty-five years. As in my days on the obstetric district in Chicago, I didn't get much sleep! Sometimes I would have three or four operations in the morning, a couple in the early afternoon, and then be called out one, two, or three times during the night. Most difficult to take were the times when I'd just get home and into bed after one emergency and get another phone call just as I had dropped off to sleep. In any case, the next morning I was in the operating room at seven A.M. getting set up, following which I would go to visit those prospective patients who hadn't come into the hospital the night before. Was I busy!

CHAPTER XIII. 1942-1948

The Other Side of Life, Outside Medicine

(MOLLY)

When Bill had left in mid-1942 we had disposed of all the chickens. The horses, Caesar and Speck, were fed and watered by neighbors in return for the use of them and our pasture. This took some of the load off my homework.

However, Caroline and I had a large vegetable garden to look after—water, weed, cultivate, and later pick and give away or can the produce from it. Naturally there were many other growing things to be looked after—young fruit trees, lawn (which I mowed), and numerous shrubs, vines, etc., to be watered until the winter came. Caroline was a tower of strength to me, and since there was little housework she could spend a good deal of time out-of-doors which she enjoyed.

Mother had come through on her way East where she spent the summers during the war seeing much of the Dallas family, in Westchester, and the Furnesses in Washington. When she returned through Santa Fe on her way to California, Caroline took wonderful care of her while I was so busy. Mother's health was very good for most of those years.

I manned the windmill and saw to it that the pool was kept filled. It was a good thing that I did as the second year when Bill was in the Pacific the gravity tank sprang many leaks. Frequently I had to climb up and hammer wooden pegs into the holes. The time came when the windmill couldn't keep the leaky tank filled, there were no workmen of any kind available, and it was impossible to get a new tank. Caroline and I eventually had to depend on water from the pool. With garden hoses I contrived to siphon water from the pool to the back patio where I attached a faucet. So for a time we lived a rather primitive existence, carrying our water in buckets, heating it on the stove for drinking, bathing, etc.

Fortunately that didn't last too long. Bill had come back and was at Bruns Hospital in town. As he was recovering from his Pacific-acquired ailments he was at home for some weeks in early 1944. Somehow he managed to get a new ten-thousand-gallon gravity tank, and by the time he returned to duty in the P. O. W. Camp in Maryland, Los Piñones was more or less habitable. However, much as I was relieved that he was in this country, I missed him, and in some ways the place missed him more. The fruit trees had died for lack of care and water and I couldn't keep up with the weeds and many other things, but I turned into a pretty good carpenter, plumber, electrician, and handyman, so that the home didn't fall apart.

I still had Susan, the collie, and Pawnee, the Great Dane, and Jerry, the cat; all of whom were great company. Aside from my hospital records on the patients' charts, I had to send out my own bills for anesthetics and buy all my own equipment, as well as maintain it. Charlie Wilder, who was maintenance man at the hospital, was a lifesaver in the latter matter, helping me with the handling of heavy oxygen tanks as well as repairing my rather ancient anesthetic machine which I had bought from Dr. Williams before he died.

One great source of pleasure was to have so many new acquaintances throughout the small town. Often I would have some former patients come up to me on the street and say,

"Oh, Dr. Molly, you were good to me in the hospital. I got your $15 bill, can't pay it all. Is it all right if I give you some of it now? I pay rest later."

Then he or she would hand me a few dirty dollar bills and

perhaps some nickels and dimes. I would scribble a receipt on whatever paper I had in my pocket and be sure to give the person credit in my books when I got home.

The three Christmases when Bill was not at home, mother stayed with me and we usually had a few strays—people without family nearby, and dear Caroline usually cooked a wonderful dinner Christmas Eve before she went home to her family in Santa Clara Pueblo. Of her six fine brothers, five of them were in the service, which brought us still closer together.

By January 1945 I was ready for a break of more than two or three days at a time and I went East. I stayed in a posh Park Avenue apartment which Uncle Don Dallas had for business friends, and Bill joined me there. It was the first and only leave he took during the war except when he was ill. Oddly enough, in spite of his having made twelve trips across the Pacific, this was the longest period we had been separated.

New York was awful, with horrible weather, crowds, and impossible traffic conditions. However, we were happy. Phyllis and family were then in New York, George having been transferred there some time before. It was a wonderful reunion with our two one-time "daughters," Diana and "Beebi" who, in the intervening three years had grown and changed a lot. It was Bill's first and last meeting with George. They looked a bit like Mutt and Jeff with their seven inches difference in height. However, their army uniforms, American and British, and their common rank (Major) formed a surprising bond and they seemed to enjoy their brief encounter. It was also the last time that Phyl and Bill were to see each other—though none of us knew this at the time.

One amusing episode occurred when Bill and I were standing in the usual long line waiting to get into Schrafft's for luncheon one day. In our long walks through the snow and slush (no one could get a taxi or even get on a bus), we had made a bet with each other to see who could be the first one to see a smile on any stranger's face. This was the last of our five days together. As the line shortened and we were near the front, an attractive hostess approached us with a smile and soon seated us at a table. Both of us looked up at her and said, simultaneously,

"You are the first person we've seen in New York to smile!"

The smile turned slightly rueful and she replied, "Well, I just came here yesterday from Virginia—I probably won't be smiling much longer!"

Bill had to get back to the POW camp and I to Santa Fe and the hospital where some patients who were to have elective surgery were awaiting my return. My dear friend Barbara Stevenson was one of them.

By March, Bill's old troubles returned with a vengeance and he came back to Bruns Hospital in Santa Fe in miserable shape. After a few weeks he was allowed to come home and become an outpatient in the hospital. He slowly improved. I was still working full time but Caroline looked after his few needs while I was absent.

As real spring approached, mother returned from California and stayed briefly until she went on East for the summer. We all rejoiced over V-E Day and as warmer weather arrived, Bill's health improved and he started a lot of work about the place, thus helping him gradually gain in strength. By the time V-J Day arrived we had quite a party at the pool—the first real celebration we'd had in a long time.

By mid-fall the Furness family were happily shipped back to poor old England on the Queen Elizabeth which was still fitted out as a troop ship. The four of them shared one cabin but the ship was lighted after the blackout of more than five years. Mother stayed to see them off and it was a joyful leave-taking as they all knew that it wouldn't be too awfully long before they could get together again.

By the spring of 1946 many service men were returning home. Bill had gotten a medical discharge shortly after V-J Day. Now we were able to get some help on the place, as well as a certain amount of much needed materials. The old faithful windmill was taken down and replaced by a Jensen Jack oil-well type of pump. This looked so much like a rocking horse that our friend, Kay Miller, christened it Rosinante for Don Quixote's horse who had helped to displace windmills. Rosy, she is to this day. Bill Stanton, a new friend just out of the navy, was restarting his construction business, and with his skeleton crew of newly discharged Spanish boys built us a good-sized garage and workshop, with attached pump house for Rosy. They also helped us convert the battery chicken house into a very fine laundry and sewing room. Bill and I had sold our homemade batteries, and with proper windows of glass instead of plastic I knew it would make an ideal workroom for me and Caroline.

"It is much too grand and sunny a room for chickens," I said. "When you feel up to having poultry again, the old garage and stable will make a fine house for them."

This, Bill readily agreed to, and as we had given up the horses by then, he went happily to work making a fine poultry house out of the now unused building. By that summer we had young White Rock chickens, white turkey poults, and White King pigeons. Bill did all the work, with only me as occasional helper.

Bill's health seemed to improve and he resumed building rock walls and terraces along the side of the large new garage and pump house. All this led inevitably to the building of our chef d'oeuvre, the Cabaña. During our ten years on Los Piñones we had often wished for some sort of structure beside the pool, both for proper dressing rooms as well as a covered place to retire to during summer storms which were usually fleeting. I drew the plans for a twenty-by-sixteen-foot rock cabin. It was to be placed at the north end of the pool and its large twelve-foot opening overlooked the water to the lovely view of the Sandia Mountains.

Bill dug fourteen-inch trenches for the foundations, filled them with rocks and cement, and with the help of an all-purpose hand tractor we dragged the long vigas (log ceiling beams) across the foundation stones. I had asked Bill more than once how he planned to get a roof on the cabaña without some outside help. I was sure he knew what he was doing, but couldn't figure how, without any tall trees, a crane, or a "sky-hook" of some kind, we were to lift the vigas into place. In fact, our dear neighbor, Barbara Stevenson, offered to bet Bill that he couldn't do it. When Bill replied, "Do you want to bet a hundred dollars that I can't?" she backed out of the bet.

The answer, of course, was simple, as most ingenious ideas are. A few rocks at a time were cemented on top of the foundations. When the cement had hardened, one end of one viga was lifted a foot or so and placed on the low wall. This was repeated many times so that as the walls grew the vigas went up with them! We incorporated a large fireplace in the back wall, including a "gooseneck" in the chimney, and were proud that, in spite of the large opening in front, the rock fireplace drew as well as all the rest of them in the house. One end of the room was curtained off for dressing rooms, and after the roof was finished and the flagstone floor was laid we moved our homemade outdoor furniture into our "summer home." I had made dressing room curtains and covered old pillows and from then on we practically lived there in the warm months and could use this retreat for night swimming, during storms, etc., since there was always a roaring fire available.

This project took us all the summer of 1948 and cost $165 for cement and woodwork! In the twenty-five years since then, it has been one of the best loved "mountain-lake resorts" which anyone ever had. Of its many advantages in the way of picnics, outdoor cooking and sleeping and entertaining, its prime value is its accessibility—no long, difficult, or congested drives to get there, and if something is forgotten at home one only has to walk a few steps to retrieve it!

CHAPTER XIV. THIRD RETIRE-
MENT FROM MEDICINE

Illness and Worry 1948-1950

(MOLLY)

After the completion of the Cabaña at the pool Bill's health again began to deteriorate rather rapidly. He was, thank goodness, able to enjoy it but he could do little active work from then on. In October our dear Caroline had to leave us for good. Her mother, at Santa Clara Pueblo, was failing in health and Caroline knew she had to go home to take care of her. This was a great blow to us, after over twelve years, to lose this wonderful friend and helper. However, there were some compensations.

By this time a number of Santa Fe doctors had returned home. Also quite a few who had been at Bruns, the General Army Hospital, during the war had fallen in love with Santa Fe and had come to town to set up practices here. This meant that I was no longer really needed, and it was rather a relief to me after five hectic years of being on constant call for anesthetics at the hospital to be able to return to full days and nights of country living. It was also a joy to be able to spend uninterrupted hours with Bill and with mother on her spring and fall visits. (By then she had once more started her yearly trips to England.)

The pleasure was not unmixed, however. Bill's increasingly severe emphysema required frequent inhalations of oxygen as well as numerous new medications. Dear Charlie Wilder, who had helped me so often at St. Vincent Hospital, fashioned a homemade, portable oxygen machine which I could use at home. This was nothing like the compact "Bennet" machines of present days which patients can operate

157

themselves. Mother's asthma was also much worse at times, and often I hauled the machine from one end of the house to the other to administer inhalation treatments to each of them from time to time. More than once mother's congested lungs produced bouts of pneumonia. Fortunately penicillin was then available and usually this marvelous medication cleared up her infections quite rapidly.

Incidentally, the severe breathing problems suffered by both my husband and my mother simultaneously produced such a mutual understanding and appreciation of each other that they became really close and affectionate friends!

I had now become a nurse, rather than a doctor. Our family doctors, first our dear friend Sandy Alexander and later young Bergere Kenney (the son of Bill's old District Attorney pal in his earlier investigative days), gave devoted care to my patients. They even came out to our home often to see them, so that I had wonderful moral as well as medical support.

Life was not all bad or grim, however. Mother invariably improved and resumed her travels. Whenever Bill had some good hours or days he would cook, clean, or do the washing and ironing when he was unable to do any heavier work. He had done a fine job in bringing Los Piñones back into good shape in the preceding two years and we had given up the poultry. Therefore my outside work was more a pleasure than a chore. Also, when there were difficult jobs to be done, there was always help available from our young friends who had returned from military service.

In those days my chief concern was to keep Bill interested and occupied in his necessarily more sedentary life. This was really solved when I got a wire recorder, the forebear of the present-day cassette or tape players. Bill had always had the faculty of anecdote and of telling a good tale. Whenever he had the breath he would talk into this machine, and in the evenings we would play back the accounts and I assured him that somehow, someday, we would get them into print. (Although at that time I never dreamed that I would eventually do this myself, the final publishing of BILL MARTIN, AMERICAN some ten years later did fulfill that promise.) Fortunately, I had urged him to tell about his early life, the details of which I knew little. His return trip to his home in Switzerland in 1948 after thirty years brought back much of this part of his life and gave him more interest in doing this.

By the summer of 1950 Bill was really in pitiable shape. Several of his fine old friends had died. Our well-loved neighbor and friend, Dr. Harold Corbusier, was dying of cancer, and Bill was especially depressed that he could do nothing to help me on the place. About the last "bright" incident was when Pete Dozier, Caroline's brother who worked for the Corbusiers, drove both Hal and Bill in their pajamas and dressing gowns downtown to see the rodeo parade. It was the last time they saw each other. They both knew it but parted with a joke and a laugh.

On August 30 Bill shot himself. Hal Corbusier died the same day.

CHAPTER XV. DOLDRUMS

(MOLLY)

Because of Bill's barrel-shaped chest due to his violent emphysema, the bullet missed his heart and he lived two and a half days. Although he underwent drastic surgery and the situation was hopeless, he was conscious most of that time. He told me that he had left a wire recording to tell me why and how he had come to the decision to take his life. He also told all the circumstances to Chief Ben Martinez of the Santa Fe Police who had learned his police work from Bill. To each of us and to his doctor friends he said,

"I know I took the coward's way out. But do you know something? It took a hell of a lot of guts to pull that trigger!"

* * * * *

I had been much more worn down by the previous anxious months than I realized. I was completely numb. I remember little of the following days except that I listened dry-eyed to the recording, alone in the empty house. Kind friends helped send cables, etc. Mother was still in England. Dear Caroline came in from the pueblo to be with me through the funeral. Also, my dear Cousin Hughes Dallas came from New York. After we had found a nice young couple, Harriet and John Griffith, to stay in the house and look after the dogs, Hughes and I went East where I stayed with my second family, the Dallases, and awaited mother's arrival from England.

Even if I could remember the months to follow, they aren't worth writing about. I weighed 106 pounds, had a hysterectomy and then pneumonia, and was a "mess"—not worth shooting and only a trial and worry to mother and all my friends. Two things stand out even now. Among many, many fine letters of condolence, one from Anne Lane (Mrs. Franklin K. Lane, a great friend of mother's and mine) stated,

"Remember, Molly—'No greater love can ever be shown than that of the one who gives his life for another.' "

The other thing was a letter some months later from the "powers that be" in Washington stating in substance, "After thorough investigation of the circumstances of your husband's death our records will show that he died as a result of disabilities acquired in *active* duty in the service of his country. You will be paid a widow's pension accordingly."

Although I later went back to Billings hospital for a refresher course in anesthesia and tried to resume practice, it didn't work and I wasn't really needed.

One of my close friends said, "Molly, you are trying to fight your way out of a paper bag!"

I was, but I couldn't find any opening and didn't have the physical, moral, or mental strength to even poke a hole in it.

CHAPTER XVI. REAWAKENING

(MOLLY)

By the early spring of 1952 mother planned a trip for us. This was good for us both to get away—really away—from all that was so dear and familiar to me but which was also such a constant reminder of my loss.

The nice Parker Wilson family were happy to take over Los Piñones for an indefinite period while they planned to look for a permanent home to buy. More than once in the preceding months I had thought seriously of selling the entire place. Many widows do this sort of thing much too quickly and regret the decision later. My usual good fortune saved me from doing the same. In the six or seven months the Wilsons lived at and enjoyed my ranch home I had a complete change, developed new perspectives, and became once more a rational human being.

Mother's plan was for us to go to Italy first and, as the warmer weather came, to work our way north to England. We both wanted to revisit some of the places in Europe we'd seen before and also take in numerous areas neither of us had visited. It didn't work out quite that way. Soon after the Dallas family saw us off on the Saturnia, bound for Genoa and Naples, mother became very ill with high fever. I was distraught, to say the least, but I had a good supply of antibiotics with me. Periodically she became better and even came out on deck a few times. Aside from outstandingly delicious Italian food and some pleasant chats with a forlorn man whose wife had been left standing at the pier because her passport was out-of-date, there was little to redeem those twelve days of almost constant anxiety. However, I realized later that for the first time in almost two years I was taken completely out of myself and had lost my disgusting self-pity for good!

Genoa was a delightful port, and with a stewardess to look after mother who was somewhat better, the kind purser took me for a drive over that beautiful city and to luncheon with his family. Naples was another matter! The famed harbor, which I was seeing for the first time, impressed me not at all. When we docked, it was a madhouse! With all of mother's and my things packed and mother fully dressed, lying on her bunk, I spent over three hours sitting on the stairway near the exit to the gangway waiting for a wheel-chair for mother who was certainly in no shape to walk more than a few feet.

Gesticulating, shouting Italian porters plus hordes of offi-cials, not to mention passengers, dashed hither and yon, stumbling over the coats and bags at my feet. Periodically some man in naval uniform told me that the wheelchair, long since ordered, would soon appear. It never did! In the midst of all the turmoil I recalled a remark of my sister's, made some time before.

"One used to say in the old days, 'See Naples and die.' Now I say, 'See Naples and drop dead!' "

Finally, when practically everyone had left the ship, a nice young officer came up to me with a porter who was wheeling a baggage cart! With great embarrassment the officer said, "I don't believe it, but I'm told there is not a single wheel-chair in the port of Naples!"

With considerable effort we hoisted mother and all the bags onto the cart and it was maneuvered down the gang-way and to the customs desk. There the tired official took one look at us, checked the bags, and waved us on to a taxi.

Amazingly enough, mother seemed much better the next day when our hired car and chauffeur drove us to Sorrento. There we had lovely, peaceful, relaxing days in that beauti-ful spot and even made the famous Amalfi drive. It was a glorious day and mother was almost her normal self, chat-ting happily about her long horse-and carriage-trek over this same route fifty-nine years before.

The drive to Rome was beautiful that lovely spring, but the week we spent in that magnificent city was a mixture of good and bad. On the plus side I revisited many of the well remembered places Addy Mueller and I had enjoyed in 1929, many on foot and some by horse and carriage. Mother was able to take only one drive about the city. Her fever returned and soon I had administered all of the medications I had brought with me for our planned two- or three-month jaunt through the rest of Italy as well as France.

I telephoned Phyllis in England and said we wanted to come to her immediately. The next day we were on a plane for London where George met us. He wanted to take mother directly to a hospital but she would have none of it and we took the three-hour drive to Malmesbury in Wiltshire.

Mother went to bed, slept twenty-four hours, and amazingly but quite characteristically for her, awoke the next day feeling perfectly normal!

After a few days' rest and assuring myself that mother was really all right, I quickly shed my responsibilities and flew to Geneva. I had written Bill's family that I wanted to meet them all. There I had an unforgettable two weeks getting to know twenty-eight in-laws—ages eighty-eight to two, none of whom spoke a word of English. My long unused French came back and we laughed, sang, ate bread and cheese together, as well as consuming delicious Swiss wines. One brother-in-law, Francois Ceppi had the only family car and saw to it that I became acquainted with most of that gorgeous country through their eyes. In a way that was one of the happiest two weeks in my life and I almost wept when the time came to leave. Next to Santa Fe, Switzerland is the only place I should like to live in the rest of my life.

Mother was not the only one to recover. I was a new woman and ready to get on with life.

CHAPTER XVII. THE BOOK

1952-1956

(MOLLY)

As I mentioned earlier, mother had always felt that she had printer's ink in her blood. She never once, that I can remember, urged Phyllis or me to write anything or even try to do so. However, she was pretty much of a perfectionist in her use of words and did her best to instill in us a desire to express our thoughts in the clearest possible manner.

Much as I loved good reading, it never had occurred to me even to want or try to write anything except a reasonably decent letter. In my sixteen years in Santa Fe I had become acquainted with a number of professional writers and admired their work. Even when I got Bill the wire recorder and had him tell many of his experiences and at times wrote some of them down in order to keep him interested, I regarded it in the light of occupational therapy for him. At that time I just hoped that I could eventually find someone who might write up his stories and adventures.

Now, in the fall of 1952, mother and I came home to Santa Fe, but the Wilson family was still at Los Piñones and would be there until Christmas. We moved into La Posada, an inn in the center of town, and I suddenly knew that Bill's story had to be told and that I was the one to do it. The next day I went out to the storeroom at my ranch and dug out Bill's large scrapbooks, his voluminous files, the wire recorder, and all the reels of wire and moved them into our apartment. The following day I started to work.

First I read the newspaper articles and letters in the scrapbooks. Then I selected from the files the case records

167

which were very familiar to me and which I thought were unusual or would be most interesting to read. My room was soon strewn with documents and papers of all sorts. Since we were only a block or two from the center of town and mother was well, she could walk to movies or to see friends. Also, the Inn had a fine restaurant, and with our apartment kitchenette for breakfasts and snacks I had few if any chores to distract me from the job at hand.

After selecting a number of Bill's cases and organizing the papers for them, I "neated up" my room, got out the wire recorder, and sat down to listen to his accounts of his early life with which I was least familiar. It wasn't easy, at first, to hear his voice two years after his death but I soon became absorbed in the story of his unusual childhood.

As anyone who has worked with the old-fashioned wire recorder knows, this machine can be maddening! At times the extremely fine wire would break and a coil of it would fly across the room. This meant frequent interruptions while untangling and tying and rewinding it. Another hurdle for me was the fact that I had never learned to type—I just used the "hunt and peck" system which was reasonably accurate but time-consuming.

However, knowing most of the story quite well, I soon got the knack of listening to a few sentences, stopping the machine and getting down the sense of the thing and making grammatical corrections and smoothing out sentences as I went along. In time it became almost second nature for me to interpolate—to add items which came back to me which he had left out in his struggle for breath while talking. Putting in several hours a day at this labor of love never wearied me. Being so sedentary also helped me gain back much of the weight I had lost in the preceding years. I was enjoying it all so much that the time flew by at such a rate that I was astonished when Christmas time approached and the nice Wilsons moved out of Los Piñones. When we moved back into our home I had finished my first draft in about six weeks!

I gave it to Jon Glidden, a dear friend who was writing stories for the *Saturday Evening Post* under the name of Pete Dawson at that time. I valued his opinion and hoped that he would be willing to struggle through it and give me his honest criticism. Imagine my elation when he brought it back the next day, saying,

"Molly, I couldn't put it down, even when guests came in last evening. I finished it about three this morning!"

This was, of course, music to my ears. Jon then gave me the name and address of his literary agent in New York. It didn't take me long to make a smooth copy of the manuscript. I carefully pasted pictures, clippings, etc., onto blank pages and inserted them into the whole package where I thought they would be relevant and serve to verify some of the more unusual incidents. This I sent off and for sometime thereafter busied myself about the ranch which needed much attention with the coming spring.

There had been periods during the preceding two years when I had seriously considered selling the whole place. Fortunately I resisted a few tempting offers and by the time the summer of 1953 came around I knew I could manage with my pension if I rented the place during the summers.

This was not difficult, with lots of open space, the swimming pool, and a pasture for horses. By the time mother went off to Europe I had the place in order and the Alfred Kings from Texas were happy to move in with their three nice children and a dog or two. They promised to look after Jerry, the cat, who was indestructible, and I moved into a charming apartment in town where my friend Kay Miller and her husband were "housesitting" in the main part of that establishment.

By this time I had finally received my manuscript back from Jon's agent and with it a kind but most discouraging letter. She stated that it was very long and rather tiresome to read. She did admit that there were some interesting incidents and that my writing wasn't too bad. However, she assured me that a biography of someone unknown was practically impossible to sell. So, that was that!

As soon as I was settled into my comfortable new quarters I was completely free to take a good second look at what I had written. I made a very early decision that the first part of Bill's life was the best written. Also, because there were no pictures, documents, letters, etc., it was the least confusing. So, on a hunch and since I had nothing to lose, I took this section of the manuscript and sent it off to Random House in New York. Then I sat down to go over the rest page by page.

In a surprisingly short time I was delighted to receive a letter from that well known publishing house. It was not only *not* a rejection slip but contained most encouraging words. The writer, Mrs. Bruce Bliven, Jr., stated that they liked the account of the young man's early experiences and even thought it was well written! Mrs. Bliven added that if the rest of the manuscript was anywhere nearly as readable, they might even consider publishing it!!

So—I again took heart and sent off the rest much as it had been originally written. This time there was considerable waiting, during which I mulled over my copy, taking one section of it at a time. I was making no progress but still keeping my spirits up because of the amazing encouragement I'd received thus far.

By late summer the large manuscript came back with a kind note saying that the balance of the story didn't measure up in any way to the first part. It was felt that much work needed to be done on it. Kind Mrs. Bliven did add that if and when I might be coming East she would be glad to go over the work with me and might be able to give me some helpful suggestions. I wrote her a grateful note and that was the end of "Chapter I" for me.

Mother and I moved back to Los Piñones and there was as usual much to be done on the ranch, so for a good many weeks I forgot about being a "writer" and enjoyed my out-of-doors work of gardener, handyman, carpenter, etc., not to mention being cook, cleaning woman, and occasional nurse for mother who was again periodically ill.

During the winter and following spring I sent the BILL MARTIN off to a few other publishers including the University of Oklahoma Press, all of whom after long delays sent me regular rejection slips. At one point mother, who was always encouraging, read aloud to me a squib from (I think it was the *Saturday Review*) her current reading.

"Listen to this, Molly. 'A very weary editor of a publishing house, the other day put down an enormous, handwritten manuscript which he had just finished. He ran his hand through his hair, trying to think of something to put on the rejection slip. Because he was a kind but honest man he finally penned—'We are sorry to be returning your paper, but you had written on it.'!!! Now, my dear, you haven't had anything like that yet?"

We both burst into laughter.

The days went swiftly by. Mother again went off to Europe and I again rented my home to the King family and moved into a one-room tiny house in town; complete with files, manuscript, wire recorder, and determination. That summer of 1954 I completely rewrote the book except for the early part which Random House had approved. Actually I didn't make too many changes; I was too green and just plain didn't know what to do to improve it. However, the actual "paper I had written on" was rather battered from its trips through the mail, so the new copy did look physically "face-lifted."

Off it went again to a New York firm, I think it was Houghton-Mifflin. By the end of that summer I was going East for two reasons. One was to go to see my father who was then living in Washington. It had been many years since I had seen him. He had written me sporadically but I had by that time little feeling for him. Though he had been only one hundred miles away when I was so very ill in 1931, he had never once come to see me.

After Bill died, he wrote me an affectionate letter and asked how I was doing. When I replied that I had been having a very rough time indeed, he never answered—didn't write again for a year. Now I had heard through mutual friends that he had been ill, and I decided that it was my duty to at least go to see him since I would be in the East in any case.

My other reason for making the trip was that mother was making her first transatlantic flight home from England at age seventy-nine. She wasn't quite sure how she would be feeling on arrival, and since Uncle Don Dallas had had a stroke she didn't want to be a possible burden on that family.

Little did I know the real reason for going to the east coast that particular year! My nine-hour luncheon reunion with my former 'round-the-world beau! (See Chapter IV.)

I had written Mrs. Bliven that I was going to New York and would appreciate an interview with her which she had graciously suggested. I had also written the New York publisher who I knew was rejecting my manuscript, to please hold it and I would call for it in person. That I did, and took it with me when I went to see Mrs. Bliven who generously gave me a good deal of time as well as some valuable suggestions. I also had the pleasure of meeting the famous Bennett Cerf.

One other item of interest to me on that visit to New York was an interview with Dr. Milton Helpern. During one of my more discouraged periods the previous months I had seriously thought of considering a new career. Because of my medical background plus my weeks of going over many of Bill's criminal investigative cases I had become quite interested in the subject of forensic medicine. I was not yet fifty years old and though I was quite determined to get my book published, I had no dreams of becoming a writer. I had written Dr. Helpern and his colleague, Dr. Gonzales, for an interview to see if it might be at all feasible for a woman to enter the field of legal medicine.

I still remembered a day shortly before Bill Martin and I were married. He had been up north of Santa Fe on an investigation of a murder of a Spanish-American who had been shot and then dumped on his mother's doorstep one night and left there to die. By that time there had been a law passed in New Mexico which stated that no autopsies could be performed by anyone except a coroner or other physician if such were within fifty miles of the deceased. Bill, always law-abiding when possible, had brought the dead man into Santa Fe and deposited him with Bill Roberts, one of the very few undertakers (morticians to you, today) in town. Bill had phoned several of his doctor friends with no luck—they were all catching babies, playing golf, or fishing. So he phoned me, saying.

"Dear, I invited you to lunch today at La Fonda but I need your help first. Will you meet me at number such-and-such on Palace Avenue in about a half an hour?"

I said of course I would. The number turned out to be Bill Roberts' workroom! My Bill met me at the door and apologetically told me his problem, adding,

"I'll do the cutting if you'll only be good enough to supervise. All I need to do is get the bullets for ballistic examination and ascertain the cause of death."

This was done, and I always accused Bill thereafter of bringing me a dead man for an engagement present! When I later wrote about the episode to friends at Billings hospital in Chicago one of my pathologist classmates, Charlie Dunlap, sent us a complete, portable autopsy kit! Fortunately I was never called upon to use it as my knowledge of anatomy and especially pathology was getting rather rusty by that time.

In any case, Dr. Helpern had granted me an interview in New York, and on the appointed day I appeared at Bellevue Hospital. I was told by a secretary to go to a certain room in a certain building and soon found myself in the New York City Morgue dissecting room! The interview was conducted among the cadavers while Dr. Helpern and Dr. Gonzales were prowling around the innards of a man who had died very suddenly after being shot in the abdomen. Cause of death was the rather surprising complete severing of the abdominal aorta by the single shot.

I rather suspect that Dr. Helpern thought it a pious idea to have the interview with this unknown female under these circumstances. Anyway, I didn't faint or turn a hair, so he granted me quite a bit of his time to discussing schools, etc., where I might go for education in the field of forensic medicine. As it turned out, my life proceeded along different lines later, but I did send him a copy of BILL MARTIN, AMERICAN which he acknowledged in a letter in which he said he now understood why a woman might be interested in this necessary but rather unpleasant field!

Back home again in the fall of 1954, there was as usual much to do about the place to get it ready for winter. Mother had persuaded Phyllis to bring Liz (Beebi) over with her the following summer. They had not been back to the United States for over nine years. Therefore, knowing that I should not be renting Los Piñones again for some time, I decided we must once more have some dogs on the place. By then we

173

had had two Great Danes and several collies, all of whom had died. Jerry, the calico cat who was still going strong even though she was over sixteen, had had numerous progeny, all of whom were born dead, and also had had one cesarean operation and a hysterectomy!

I heard that the State Penitentiary was giving up its bloodhounds and had puppies for sale. I went to see Bill's old friend Mr. Brunk who was still warden there who told me that if I would take the two remaining males he'd let me have them for half price since they would be going to the Bill Martin home! Happily, but as it turned out, unwisely, I brought the two adorable, amazingly ugly Rufus and Rollo home with me. We did enjoy their ridiculous antics and they certainly brought a good deal of LIFE to the place for the next year. However, they were not only all over the immediate neighborhood but wandered miles afield. They lost their dog tags and collars, howled under the neighbors' windows at five A.M., and generally drove me and everyone else frantic! I finally had to pen them up in the old chicken house and yard when there was a bad rabies scare in town, including one human case. They were the only dogs I ever had which I could not train to some degree. I felt ashamed of myself but found a home for them on a ranch about two hundred miles away.

BACK TO WRITING

In early 1955 I was chatting with Dorothy Greenwood in her well known bookstore, the Villagrá, when she said, "Molly, why don't you send your manuscript to the Caxton Printers in Idaho? They are interested in new writers and especially anything concerning the West. Certainly, knowing as much as I do about your Bill's life out here, it must be quite a tale."

At that I said, "Dorothy, would you be willing to read it?"

When she said she'd love to, I turned it over to her that day. She read it in a very short time and told me to send it by all means, which I did.

Once more I felt that there still might be some hope. As winter set in and mother had gone off to California, there was little for me to do except shovel snow and chase down my rambunctious puppies. I had closed off mother's apartment to save on heat, so there was relatively little housework. I suddenly thought about my reunion with Addy the previous fall and determined to unearth my letters from around the world and read them over. I'd not looked at them since 1929. After not too much searching I found them in the storeroom and settled down to read.

After a quarter of a century I not only relived that wonderful trip in detail but was amazed to find the letters quite readable. Having nothing better to do I got out the typewriter and "composed," if you'd call it that, "The Nine-Hour Luncheon." It was great fun as well as making me realize again how fortunate I had always been. It was too short for a book and really too long for an article—but I gaily sent it off to about three magazines, one after another. To my amazement I got only one rejection slip! The other two magazines were kind enough to write letters stating that they thought the manuscript quite readable and interesting but not exactly suitable for their particular publications.

By this time summer was approaching—there was work to be done. However, what brought my heightened encouragement to real elation was a letter from Mr. Gipson at The Caxton Printers saying that they were definitely interested in BILL MARTIN, AMERICAN. He added that there was probably a good deal of work to be done on the manuscript. However, they suggested that I send it to Mr. Alan Swallow in Denver. Mr. Swallow had his own publishing firm but had done a good deal of editorial work for them and others. *If* Mr. Swallow would take on the job and put the thing in shape, they, Caxton, would probably publish it.

It didn't take long for me to send the manuscript to Denver with a covering letter. I received a polite reply from Mr. Swallow saying that he would take on the job. From there on I felt free as a bird and we all had a wonderful summer at Los Piñones, including the happy visit of my sister and her younger daughter. The latter was amazing. She had left Santa Fe at age five-and-a-half. At age nineteen on her return to Los Piñones she remembered infinite details of her childhood on the ranch, many of which I had forgotten.

175

We had a large party up at the pool and the Cabaña which she and Phyllis had never seen, and the guests comprised all those who had known her as a small child.

Some seven or eight months later, along in the spring of 1956, mother and I were discussing the question of renting Los Piñones in future summers. As Phyllis's girls were of marriageable age, mother had generously given my sister a fair sum of money as her well looked after finances were in very good shape. Always being scrupulously fair, she had given me a similar amount. Having no children I really didn't need it, but naturally accepted it gratefully.

The logical thing for me to do was to remodel my home so that it would be more rentable to families during the summer months. So I went happily back to my old drawing board and drew plans for the changes. Our friend and neighbor Bill Stanton drew up a contract with me and said he and his fine men would be able to start in early June. Mother would be leaving for England about that time and I planned to camp out in the cabaña at the pool during the period the house would be torn up.

Just as our plans were shaping up, Phyllis wrote that her older daughter, Diana, who was then halfway through a nursing course in London, had become quite ill. She asked if her daughter could spend the summer with me while recuperating. I immediately wrote that I'd love to have her if she could stand "camping out" at the Cabaña. I did have an alternative in that we could housesit for friends who were going to Europe for two months.

Diana arrived shortly before mother was to leave—then everything happened at once! Alan Swallow returned my manuscript with an apologetic letter for keeping it so long. Then, to my amazement, he stated that once he had gotten down to it he had removed all of the many pages of clippings, letters, pictures, documents, etc. He then read it through and found there were very few changes to be made—so few, in fact, that he cut his charge to a fraction of what he had first quoted, and added, "Why didn't someone think of that before?"

Actually, when I reread it, I found it astonishingly similar to my very first draft, written in late 1952. The "paper I'd written on" was quickly dispatched to The Caxton Printers, and the following waiting period didn't seem, in prospect, so long or so hopeless.

The next thing that happened was that the workmen were ready to start breaking through the walls, having finished all the outside additions to the house. Mother had a routine physical examination, which she always did before starting across the ocean. Dr. Bergere Kenney discovered that she had diabetes. He said he wouldn't dare let her start out until she had had her diet and medication well regulated. This was the first and only time in mother's 46 transatlantic crossing that we had to cancel her reservations.

The main problem facing us was where to go in the meantime. We couldn't hold up the busy construction workers in the midst of their best building season. Dear Louise Corbusier came to our rescue. She offered her guest house to the three of us as long as necessary. We gratefully moved in and some of the housewalls were broken open the next day. In about two and a half weeks Bergere said that mother might travel. She was fortunate enough to get a Chicago to London flight. I escorted her to Chicago while Barbara Stevenson took Diana up to their mountain cabin.

On our respective returns, Diana seemed very well and insisted that we "camp out" in the Cabaña. I was pleased to do this as it meant that I could be right on the spot to oversee the building, just as Bill and I had done years before. Mother's apartment living room was made over into an attractive dining room with a glassed-in porch added as a gracious entrance from the main living room to it. My kitchen was completely done over and enlarged so that it connected directly with the former kitchenette which then became a pantry. A large bath was added to the master bedroom and Bill's former study was enlarged and opened out into a sunny patio which adjoined the new bath.

Everything turned out beautifully, although it took much longer and cost much more than originally planned as I kept having the men do far more than we'd contracted for. Hence I had to take out the first mortgage, and the only one I ever had. However, the results were worth it.

The high point of that summer was the acceptance of my

book and a contract that came with the letter. Dorothy Greenwood happened to be sitting in the Cabaña when I brought the mail home. In addition to this, the design for the cover, the end sheets, and the jacket which my dear friend Fran Owen had done, arrived, and that, to me, made it a real BOOK! Little did I know that it would be almost two and a half years more before the busy Caxton Printers would deliver the actual volumes.

CHAPTER XVIII. RETURN TO MEDICINE, GERONTOLOGY

1957-1960

(MOLLY)

The winter-spring of 1956-57 were most exciting for the Radford "girls." Both of Phyllis's daughters became engaged, Diana to an American, Tom Carpenter, who was the son of Phyllis's oldest friend, Diana's godmother. Liz's fiance was a fine British Army officer. They were to be married within six weeks of each other that coming summer. That, of course, settled the matter again of my renting the newly remodeled home.

In spite of my having gone into debt the previous summer, mother persuaded me, without much difficulty, to have Bill Stanton remodel the old garage-stable-chicken house, making it into a guest house. She generously said she'd pay for it as she was giving Phyllis additional money for the girls' trousseaux and weddings.

So the well built but empty, messy chicken house last occupied by the bloodhounds was converted into a delightful if tiny guest house with living room, bedroom, bath, and kitchenette. Los Piñones was growing into quite an estate undreamed of at the time Bill and I first looked down into the hole in the ground" twenty-years before. I now had a Casita Gallina (Little Chicken House).

The Alfred Kings were delighted to rent the newly made-over and enlarged place for the summer. They had missed it very much during the two previous seasons when it had not been available. Mother and I had reservations on the Queen Elizabeth for mid-June. Meantime I had been urged by some of my doctor friends to return to some kind of medical work and become useful once more. The head of the New Mexico Department of Public Health in Santa Fe said to me one evening at a County Medical dinner.

"Molly, if you don't want to go back into active practice, why don't you consider Public Health work? It isn't strenuous and we need people like you."

"Well, Stanley, it's a thought but I'm completely rusty on all things medical and I'm sure I'm too old to go back to school—I'm now fifty-two. Besides, what sort of field might I be fitted for?"

"Nonsense, one is never too old to go back to school, and you're not old at all," said Dr. Leland flatteringly. Then he added, "There is now much interest in gerontology and I want to open up a division for that in my department. I'll make a deal with you. You go and take a year's Public Health course at any university you want and I'll give you the job of heading up and developing your own new division in any way you see fit."

Now there was a challenge! What interested me most was that I might be my own boss; also, the job would be far from routine, as it was quite a new field where one might use one's imagination. I seriously doubted if I could discipline myself to study again, or even qualify for a good school of Public Health. However, after mulling it over and discussing it with other M.D. friends, I dug up my medical school records and sent them to the University of California at Berkeley with an application for their School of Public Health.

To my surprise, I was accepted for the year beginning the next autumn. I had chosen Berkeley as I had always loved the San Francisco area ever since I'd entered the Golden Gate in 1928 before the bridge was built. My brief wartime visits there to meet Bill each time he came out of the Pacific increased my fascination for that beautiful bay. Also, I felt that was one large metropolitan area I could bear to live in with my inbred love of country living.

So we began to make long-range plans before starting for the weddings in England. Then a real and serious complication arose just about ten days before we were to leave and the Kings were to move in.

One morning mother came into my sunny kitchen for

180

breakfast. She had been in very good health and form. Her diabetes had practically disappeared, with her religiously following her diet and wisely losing a good deal of weight. As she lifted a spoonful of cantaloupe to her mouth, she said,

"Oh, I wanted to ask you——I wanted to ask you—ask you—ask you" Her face took on a blank look as she repeated the words just like a phonograph needle stuck in a worn groove on a record. She turned very pale but displayed no other signs or symptoms. I led her to a couch where she lay down and was completely silent but neither asleep nor unconscious.

Fortunately I was able to reach Bergere Kenney and he came out immediately. He gave her a thorough neurological going over. She smiled and could speak to him and followed his directions obediently. She had no paralysis but very poor coordination. With eyes closed she could not touch her nose with her finger, etc.

Bergere and I went into another room and mother promptly lay down and went to sleep.

Bergere said, "You know, of course, that she has had a slight stroke." I nodded. He continued, "I know your plans—when were you intending to leave for England?"

When I said in a little over a week, he said, "If it were anyone else but your mother that 'Woman of Iron,' I would say cancel everything. However, I'm willing to bet that this will pass and she may not have another for weeks, months, or years. If, as I expect, she recovers completely from this, you'd never forgive yourself for depriving her of going to her granddaughters' weddings." Then he added, "It is your decision, you are a doctor, you'll be with family and friends along the way, and I'm sure you can cope with whatever situation arises."

With that he left, telling me to phone him if anything came up before we left, wished me luck and kissed me good-bye.

That trip was something to remember! I must say I don't recall many details. My worry over mother and whether I was doing the right thing was on my mind the entire five thousand miles. Mother slept a good deal of the time on the Super Chief and on the Twentieth Century. In Chicago her old friend Marie Smith had invited a few others to her apartment on Lake Shore Drive. She arranged for mother to rest in her bedroom and each dear friend had a short chat alone with mother who seemed her normal self except for being unusually quiet. It was to be the last time she was to see any of them, which, fortunately, none of them realized. All seemed to enjoy their many reminiscences of the past sixty-odd years.

The following morning coming down in the New York Central along the Hudson, mother awoke and looked across the double compartment at me and said, "What happened to me that morning before we left home?"

I replied, "You had a slight stroke and it affected your speech, but you are all right now."

Her response was, "Oh!"

We saw all the Dallas family at the lovely farm home in Katonah, and some of them saw us off on the Queen Elizabeth two days later. On the comfortable ocean crossing, mother spent many hours in her deck chair and gradually grew stronger. By the time Phyllis met us at the pier mother was almost her old self and there was much to interest her in the coming weddings.

Mother and I stayed at enchanting Castle Coomb where we were peacefully away from all the bustle of preparations. However, each day she grew more interested in seeing the girls' trousseaux and hearing about the plans. By the time we moved to the Old Bell Inn, right next door to the famous Malmesbury Abbey where the girls were to be married, Mary Radford was reading the newspapers, chatting with old and new friends, and was her old self. I had gambled but had done the right thing!

Since I was due at the University of California in early September, I left ahead of mother, returned home to tend to things there, and re-rent Los Piñones to the J. Calvin Rutherfords for the year that I would be away. With my little car fully packed, I drove to California feeling free as air and looking forward to a completely new experience. My dear friend Kay Miller drove as far as Denver with me, and while there I went out to see Alan Swallow, whom I had never met. He was most cordial and kind, again apologizing

182

for having kept my manuscript so long. He also told me that the Caxton Printers, who published all the school books for Idaho, were notoriously slow, so I must be patient while awaiting publication of the book.

I was not worrying about mother who was then in Phyllis's home. The latter had assured me that when the time came mother would fly to Southern California to her old stamping grounds there. If necessary Phyllis would fly with her.

When I arrived in San Francisco I went directly to the home of Polly Kremer Schwartz who had been my roommate at Mount Holyoke thirty years before. I had only seen her two or three times in the intervening period. That was a grand reunion! We found ourselves just as good friends as ever.

Nevertheless, my arrival was a bit more than confusing. After our greetings, Polly handed me a telegram from Aunt Harriet in New York. It was a long one, stating that mother had decided to come home via New York and wanted to visit her sister. With Uncle Don an invalid in a wheelchair and Aunt Hat suffering from cancer, the latter just couldn't take on her sister who had so recently had a stroke. Who could blame her!?

I went to Polly's phone and called Phyllis in England and told her the story. Mother had made her own plans and reservations without telling Phyllis anything about it. Her old independent self! I told Phyllis to tell mother that unless she would let her daughters make her plans I would give up my plan to go to school, fly East to meet mother, and then we would have to find a home base. Phyllis calmed me down and said that she would take care of everything. I thanked God for the transatlantic telephone; had a good visit with Polly and her nice husband Sandy that evening.

Next morning I drove to Berkeley to the School of Public Health. After interviews there I had to find a place to live. I had allowed a few days for this but what I heard about the rental situation in that college town was not encouraging. I drove up the street along the north side of the campus just as two fire trucks screeched past me. Quickly I turned left off on the first side street, Euclid, and found a parking place at the corner. There was a drugstore across the street where I intended to consult newspapers and the phone book.

As I locked the car door I looked over my shoulder at what seemed to be an apartment house about three storeys tall. Just above me was a blank looking pair of windows—could it be an empty apartment? I went to the small lobby and pushed the bell marked Superintendent. A woman about my age opened the door.

Pointing, I said to her, "Is that apartment for rent?"

She looked me over carefully and said, "Well, yes, I guess it is. I've sprained my ankle and haven't been able to clean it up since the last tenant moved out yesterday."

"Could I please look at it? I'm a new student at the School of Public Health right over there," pointing this time across the street.

The kind woman led me up a half-flight of steps and unlocked a door to a quite spacious two-room apartment with a kitchenette. I looked out the window and saw the drugstore, a small grocery, a cleaning establishment, a bookstore, and an attractive tiny restaurant with a patio. Holding my breath I said, "I'll be here a year; how much is the rent?"

She named a modest sum for those days and I immediately said, "I'll take it and move in today. I'll clean it up." We shook hands and the deal was made.

Within an hour of my arrival in Berkeley I had a home within a short pleasant walk of my classes and with everything at hand I could possibly wish for. Again, my fabulous luck was with me. I had "caught another Brass Ring," as Bill Mauldin would say. (His latest book, called THE BRASS RING, was recently published and just the other day I heard him discuss it here in Santa Fe.)

I soon had my gear unpacked and put away in my new home. Then I drove to downtown Berkeley and made a deal to sell my car which I knew I wouldn't need until the following summer. I triumphantly drove back to Polly's to tell her my news and that, of course, I would be seeing her often.

To be back in school after over twenty years was no joke. Most of my fellow M. D. classmates, not to mention other younger nurses, nutritionists, sanitary engineers, etc., had for the most part been working more or less continuously in their fields. To me, many of the more superficial courses in organization, administration, and generalized health problems seemed quite "ivory-towerish" and more full of talk than of substance. However, if I hoped to get a job with any sort of governmental agency, these must be absorbed and it was necessary to learn the strange and verbose vocabulary.

Down-to-earth courses in epidemiology, sanitation, nutrition, and statistics had me completely floored for some time. My ability to concentrate and remember took most of my waking hours, and I was quite sure I would never make the grade.

Less than three weeks after I had started my studies, a cable came from Phyllis saying that mother was flying from London to Los Angeles and please would I meet her there. Naturally I did so. Mother, almost eighty-three stepped off the plane which had flown over the North Pole (her 46th Atlantic crossing), waved aside the wheelchair I'd had sent out to the plane, and greeted me as cheerfully as if she had just taken a short taxi ride. I got her settled in her old "bailiwick" near her friends, had a talk with her fine physician whom she had had for some years out there, and went back north.

Naturally I flew down to be with her for Christmas and at various other times and she seemed in fine health and spirits. Periodically during that school year she would telephone me and say,

"Darling, I had one of those 'funny' attacks last evening at dinner, but someone helped me to bed and I slept it off and feel fine this morning. Don't bother to come down."

Of course I knew "those funny things" were further repeated small strokes but they didn't seem to faze her or incapacitate her in any way.

By summer, when the academic year was over, I brought mother to Berkeley and settled her into an apartment across the hall from me. I had to remain to take a "field" course and write a thesis in order to get my Master's degree in Public Health. I acquired a car and traveled about the lovely countryside visiting County Health Clinics, nursing homes, hospitals, etc., and mother often went with me and enjoyed the drives. At night she would read and watch television while I worked on my paper, the subject of which was "Emphysema and Related Non-tuberculous Diseases of the Chest." It was a proper subject for one who planned to go into gerontology.

Being certain that mother was not up to a cross-country car trip, I persuaded her to go into a rest home while I drove back to Santa Fe. My tenants, the Rutherfords, had taken up their option for a second year at Los Piñones, so I had to find a place in town to live. Fortunately, our good friend Nancy Lane, whose wonderful mother had died the preceding spring, offered me her mother's apartment. Mother came back to Santa Fe under her own steam and we settled in for the year.

Dr. Leland kept his word and provided me with an office and secretary in the State Health Department and told me to go ahead and form my own new Division of Gerontology.

In the meantime Nancy Lane had bought Dorothy Greenwood's Villagra Bookstore. Dorothy had happily retired and in spite of poor health had married a fine retired navy man, Captain C. O. Ward. I had met him at their wedding a year or so before. Everyone was delighted over this happy marriage, and Dorothy was pleased over my forthcoming book.

When the advance copies and stacks of "blurbs" finally arrived in mid-spring of 1959, mother was full of enthusiasm and spent hours addressing envelopes for the blurbs to everyone we knew. She also sent many, many copies of the book to possible reviewers, school libraries, etc. We were both plenty busy doing our own advertising.

Nancy Lane ordered more copies of the book than I thought she should for her bookstore. She also generously gave me an autograph party in her and our combined apartments. The day really had come after six and a half years of waiting!

My new job proved rather a challenge, and aside from too many trips for meetings over the country, I did enjoy a good deal of it. I learned much about the facilities and lack of them for older people in my own state; gave talks to women's clubs to inform the people of what we were trying to do. Friends dropped in often and took mother out when I was busy. Among them Cap and Dorothy Ward came frequently whenever they were not off on a trip.

Toward summer a very pleasant surprise occurred. Fritz Jandrey, my old friend from the 'round-the-world trip, and his wife came to town. I hadn't seen him since the crazy trip to England in 1931. He was retiring from the State Department and they were looking for a pleasant place to live. They didn't settle in Santa Fe but did stay for some time that year.

Toward the end of the summer Cal Rutherford came to see us, begging to renew their lease on Los Piñones. However, after two years away from my home and with mother's perceptibly failing strength I said no. It was fortunate that mother did not have a quite incapacitating stroke until we were back in our own home. I got a hospital bed for her sunny remodeled room and had to have part-time nursing help since I was still working full-time at the Health Department. Now I was really "in" the practice of Gerontology! That fall I had little time for out-of-doors work on the place but was able to get some occasional help and friends were more than kind.

Mother had many visitors and for the most part she was so mentally clear that she enjoyed the calls and they enjoyed her. Dorothy Ward's health began to deteriorate, so they didn't take many trips but came weekly to see mother, and Cap and I became good friends. Phyllis flew over and stayed some time, giving mother a lift by telling her about her greatgrandchildren. Elizabeth had had a baby boy in Germany where they were stationed and Diana had had a girl in Minneapolis.

At one point mother sank into a coma and we all thought it was the end. She simply slept for over a week! Bergere said she "was hibernating." Thanks to him and to excellent nurses around the clock, she awoke one morning and asked for her usual breakfast. Amazing woman! She gradually regained strength. She could walk a few steps with help but her eyesight was failing rapidly due to brain damage and I started to read aloud to her by the hour whenever I was not at work.

Shortly after Christmas, 1959, Dorothy Greenwood died of a complete heart failure, after three extremely happy years with Cap. Uncle Don Dallas died suddenly in 1958 and we knew Aunt Hat didn't have too far to go. Marie Smith in Chicago had died about the same time that Uncle Don had. All this saddened mother but she did not dwell on it and never complained about her own incapacities.

By the spring of 1960 her condition had so deteriorated that we had to move her into the hospital where she could have constant care. Also, my life was altering in other ways. A few months earlier I had been encouraged to set up a "pilot project" for oldsters a few days a week. A twenty-five-thousand-dollar budget had been put aside for this and I was enthusiastically "drumming up" cooperation from various clinics, organizations, and our local County Health Department. Odd rumors began floating about my office which were disturbing. Finally I confronted my boss, Dr. Stanley Leland, and asked him directly, "What's going on?"

He rather shamefacedly told me that the recently elected new governor had neatly cut out the budgets for several state departments and that included my Pilot Project budget, plus my Gerontology Division. My secretary and I were soon to be out of a job. The so-called "merit system" operating in most state jobs did not allow for anyone to be "fired" without due cause. However, there seemed to be no rule or regulation which forbade the governor from removing a job from under any employee!!

Stanley added that it wouldn't happen right away and asked me to please stay on until it did. I said, "No," and handed him my resignation that day. I heard later that all the money "saved" by the budget cutting was distributed to the "deserving poor voters" in the state. I believe they got about seven dollars apiece!

This was in May. Cap Ward, bless him, had asked me to marry him and I had accepted him but we planned to wait for some time before doing so since it had been a comparatively short time after Dorothy's death. Also, I wanted to give mother a bit of time to adjust to the new situation. Cap, as well, had much to do to settle Dorothy's estate and to sort out her possessions accumulated over three marriages and living in one home for many years. She had left everything to him since she had no near relatives. He had given her the three happiest years of her whole life.

CHAPTER XIX. CAP

(MOLLY)

Clarence Oliver Ward was born in Utica, Nebraska, the fifth child of William Wilson Ward, on January 20, 1894. His mother, Olive (Sample) Ward, died at his birth and his distracted father had lost his farm and practically everything he had owned at about the same time, a bad Depression year. Because he already had four small children to look after, the baby, Oliver, was taken to a neighboring farm where he was cared for by Mrs. Susan B. Hughes and her daughter MayBelle. The wonderful woman, a Civil War widow, had a pittance to live on but gave the baby and little boy a fine start in life until he was about eight years old. The two women taught him to read and write even before he was ready to walk to the one-room "red school house" four miles away. He had no playmates, no toys, and has often said that he really had no childhood. What a complete contrast to my own background!

When he was eight years old his father considered him old enough to become a working farm hand along with his older brothers, Harry and Roy. His two sisters, May and Winnie, as teenagers did all the house work and were really mothers to their adored baby brother. As their father struggled and made good on a new farm, all of them rose at four A.M. and worked till sundown. The only schooling they had was during the winter months when the fields were deep in snow.

Oliver hated farming from the start. His father was fair with him but very strict and probably, unconsciously, re-

191

sented the boy as the unwitting cause of his beloved Olive's death. By the time the youngster was twelve, encouraged by his Uncle Ed, one of his father's brothers, he ran away from home to Ord, Nebraska. He was determined to get an education and started in at high school. He earned his living working in a drugstore, a doctor's office, a dry goods store, and other places. He never really did return home but kept in occasional touch with his two sisters.

Really wanting to study medicine but seeing no hope of even going to college, he joined the Navy upon his graduation from high school at age 17, lying about his age. He said he was twenty-one, and being a strapping youth they believed him. He was shortly shipped out to Bremerton, Washington and started his adult life as a coal passer on the cruiser Pennsylvania.

Never having had any childhood diseases or even shots for them, he was vaccinated on entering the Navy and some time later had such a badly infected arm that he appeared at the sick bay. His "boss" in the coal bunker was furious but it was obvious that the boy-man was unfit for heaving coal! The immaculate white walls, sheets, etc., of the sick bay looked like heaven to the grimy lad and he soon wangled a transfer and became a hospital corpsman.

During the two following years, he never gave up his dream for further education. To this day he has never been willing or able to tell me just how he managed an appointment to the Naval Academy at Annapolis. However, he did so. He never met the senator who sent in his name. There were complications in respect to his lied-about age which was too old to get him into the Academy. However, that was straightened out and his true age of nineteen was duly recorded.

He arrived at the Naval Academy as a Blue Jacket, the first enlisted man to do so. He spent the summer of 1913 studying for competitive examinations, but in the meantime he still worked full time as a hospital corpsman and an enlisted man. With some helpful tutoring he passed and entered as a plebe.

He is too modest even to tell me of his career at Annapolis, but I do know that there is a plaque in the Field

House with his name on it as the outstanding member of the class of 1917. I saw it when we went back to his fiftieth class reunion in 1967. This I also know—he was president of his class for four years; he played football on the Navy team for four years, being captain of the team his last year. He was also on the wrestling team and on the navy crew throughout; and was called "Cap" by his classmates long before he even became an ensign.

During his happy four years at the Academy (he always said he had never learned to "play" at anything until then), he became quite well acquainted with Josephus Daniels, then Secretary of the Navy. The latter quizzed him about getting into the Academy as an enlisted man and said, "Why can't others do the same in the future?" The result was that many men do that these days—once selected they are relieved of all duty while studying for their entrance examinations.

The class of 1917 graduated two months early, in April instead of June. It was said that this was done so that the United States might get into the war with proper naval officers! Cap married Constance Wait, a Cornell graduate, in New York where her father was a prominent lawyer. The next day he was shipped out to France. On summer midshipmen cruises he had been many places and was on the first navy ship to go through the Panama Canal in 1915. He was in Ville Franche, France, when war was declared in August 1914. Cap spent World War I on a destroyer, the Monaghan #32, doing convoy duty for American supply and troop ships going into Brest, France. They spent countless weeks at a time in and out of the Bay of Biscay, some of the roughest water on earth.

Post-war, Cap stayed in the Navy, on destroyers. His last command was the McDougal #54, which he put in "moth balls." At that time a crewman came to him holding a filthy painting he had found in a forward locker, saying,

"Skipper, what'll I do with this?"

Cap, seeing that it was something framed, said, "Just put it there, I'll look at it later."

Much later he found after cleaning it up that it was a copy of "The Return of the Mayflower," a quite well known painting of six "four-stackers" coming into the English Channel and being greeted by some French fishermen. The artist had made copies for each of the six destroyer captains whose ships were depicted in the painting. These were the first destroyers—twelve-hundred tonners—to cross the Atlantic soon after our entry into the war. The British had said it never could be done! The McDougal had been one of the six, and Cap fell heir to the picture which now graces our living room wall.

One other memento of that ship is a beautiful small model made of it given to Cap by an old navy friend. That now rests above our mantelpiece at Los Piñones.

I have tried to get Cap to tell his own story. He writes far better than I. However, he says he is too happy and busy in our idyllic advancing years to do so. Therefore, this is my own story, and I have to do the best I can with his to give a proper background for this account of the remaining and "best years of our lives."

Cap resigned from the Navy in 1921, hoping to save his marriage which was far from a happy one. Secretary Daniels would not accept his resignation but when Daniels was absent Cap presented the resignation to the Assistant Secretary of the Navy, Franklin Delano Roosevelt, who accepted it.

After his resignation from the Navy, Cap had several civilian jobs from Wall Street to Boy Scout executive, but his most interesting jobs were in the field of consulting engineering, all of them being in the East—New York, Philadelphia, Boston, Connecticut, etc. When World War II came he joined the Navy Reserve and served from 1941-1948, first in shipbuilding and later in personnel.

Cap and Connie had three boys. The first one, Clarence Oliver, Jr., died soon after birth in 1920. William Wait was born in 1922, and John Westlake was born in 1925. Bill, the older boy, enlisted in the Marines as a private and had a wonderful time until the "powers that be" found that he was a graduate engineer from Cornell. They promptly gave him a commission and transferred him to a teaching position in the Seabees. He was furious and sure that his father was responsible! John, at 17, joined the Coast Guard, then enlisted in the Navy.

194

After the war Bill married a delightful girl, Kathleen Livingston, in 1945 and then started studying medicine. He and Kay did it on their own, refusing financial help from C. O., as Bill calls his father. Before John got out of the service, Cap was demobilized (he was later called back for more personnel work).

In an effort, again, to salvage their marriage, Cap and Connie took a fabulous bicycle trip over much of the world, including Japan and China and then to the South Seas. They cycled seven thousand miles in Australia and several more in New Zealand. Cap quite definitely planned to retire in Christ Church in the latter country. From there they took a freighter halfway around the world to Europe and bicycled over much of that. It was a remarkable trip but did little to patch up the marriage.

On their return they found son John had been medically discharged from the Service in bad shape. Cap devoted the next several years to helping rehabilitate his younger son and seeing that he finished his education. After traveling over the country they decided that the University of New Mexico branch college at Las Cruces was the place for them. Father and son went through four years of college together there and graduated in 1954, thirty-seven years after Cap had graduated from the Naval Academy!

Cap divorced Connie that year and he and John spent a year raising chickens in Las Cruces until John obtained a job at White Sands and was on his own. Cap then traveled about the United States—east to see Dr. Bill and Kay and west to become reacquainted with his two sisters in California, May Gonnela and Winnie Tatlow. It was through them that he began to receive news of his old classmates from Ord High School whom he had not seen or heard from since he ran away to sea in 1911.

To get ahead of my story a bit: the surviving members of that class of eighteen, six boys and twelve girls, Roxy Severn, Clara Belle King, Ruth Cushing, Lenore Nichols, came to Santa Fe for a reunion in 1965; also, classmates Mabel Robinson and husband Ray, Lillian Severyn and husband Charles, Ruth Flynn and husband Leslie, and Arthelia Ramsey and husband William. The surviving husbands and I were "the out-laws." Cap was the only surviving male classmate. We all had a wonderful time and became friends. Ever since, those who still survive write a "Round Robin," so two or three times a year hear all one another's news.

The last time we saw one another was at the *sixtieth* high school class reunion in Ord, Nebraska in 1971!

To go back to 1956: Cap returned periodically to his and John's home in Las Cruces. There he met Dorothy Greenwood who was visiting friends in that town. She had been widowed not too long before and had very precarious health. She and Cap became great friends and corresponded extensively for the next year.

In January 1957 they were married in her Santa Fe home in the presence of about twenty friends. I was among the guests and met him for the first time at his wedding!

CHAPTER XX. IDYLLIC ADVANC-
ING YEARS

Ups and Downs 1960-61

(MOLLY)

I had never visualized the possibility of marrying again. Naturally, as a widow for ten years, there were times when I dreamed that there *might* be another man in my life. Now in May 1960 the incredible had happened! Cap at 66 and I at 55 were unquestionably in love! I insisted that he was "a young man in a hurry" and felt that he should take a bit more time before embarking on a third marriage so soon after his very happy three years with Dorothy.

What really decided the matter was that mother, in the hospital, was failing mentally and we both felt that if we were to marry we should do so while she was really aware of what was happening. So we picked June second and I had announcements ordered in mother's name for that date.

What followed was almost a farce!We consulted the Reverend Robert Boshen, the Presbyterian minister, told him our story, and asked if he would be willing to marry us at mother's bedside. He said he would be happy to do so. Then we asked our respective doctors, Charles McGoey and Bergere Kenney, if they would stand up with us as our witnesses at 11 A.M. in the course of making their hospital rounds, and they agreed.

On May thirty-first we went to the County Courthouse for the license and there we were asked for our blood-test reports. Here were a couple of "old poops" who had neglected to have the tests made. I had been with the State Health

197

Department until very recently, albeit in the Gerontology Division, Cap had been married less than four years before, and neither of us knew that a state law requiring tests for V. D. had been passed in the meantime!!

We dashed to the Santa Fe laboratory, telling our friends there that we needed blood tests right away. Dr. Marcus Smith, in charge of the lab, said they couldn't get out the reports in less than two days! Then he took pity on us and said that if we'd go to Dr. Harry Ellis across the street in the hospital lab he could take care of "shot-gun" cases in a few hours. We crossed to the hospital, had our blood samples taken, and amid smirks from the personnel, most of whom we knew, were told to come back in two hours.

We killed the time by picking up the wedding ring which had been engraved, and returned to the hospital. There our amused friend delivered us the documents, saying, "Aren't you relieved that they are negative?!"

From there we recrossed Palace Avenue to Dr. Kenney's office for his signature. Bergere's nice secretary, Frances Moresford said, "Oh, the doctor is in the TB clinic—he'll be there all afternoon."

We then said we'd go next door to Dr. McGoey for the signatures.

Frances said, "Oh, he's at the same clinic at the County Health Department."

Thereupon we got in the car and drove to the clinic. Elbowing our way through crowds of mothers and children we reached the busy doctors and told them our story.

Taking the two papers from us, Charlie said to Bergere, "They can't even wait till we get back to our offices."

"Well," we replied in unison, "we've still got to get our license when the County Clerk's office is open."

Bergere, grinning, said, "They've got us coming and going. First they interrupt our busy clinic and Thursday we'll have to break into our hospital rounds to stand up with them! Have you ever been a bridesmaid, Charles?"

"No, not even a bride!"

With much laughter they signed the blood reports and waved us off, saying, "See you at the wedding—just hope we don't get called out on emergency at eleven o'clock. It still won't be legal without 'bridesmaids!' "

Norma Dozier, our dear Caroline's sister-in-law, was mother's nurse on duty. Thursday morning she had fixed up a table with a white cloth, put on it a lovely bunch of flowers which Cap had ordered, and a bottle of mother's favorite wine which I had ordered. She had mother all arrayed in a new bed jacket and propped up in her bed. Mother, bless her, was perfectly clear mentally and all smiles. She loved Cap, as he did her.

Robert Boshen appeared a few minutes early and the two dear doctors arrived on the dot of eleven. The knot was tied, the marriage certificate was signed, and we all had a glass of the lovely wine together. I couldn't help thinking back to my first marriage in the Casa Gallina (the Chicken House) twenty-three years earlier to Bill. What a lucky gal I was to have encountered two such wonderful men! No fancy church weddings ever compared with my two, one in a chicken house, the other in a hospital!

On our way to lunch at La Fonda and then home to Los Piñones we talked of our good fortune and the fact that we had first met at a wedding!

We had each written all of our friends about our coming marriage as well as sending them announcements. Nan and Eastburn Smith, close neighbors and good friends, gave us a small but lovely reception two days later at their home. Invited were Cap's and my closest friends who had been slightly indignant, but understanding, about not being able to be present at the actual ceremony.

Everyone we knew seemed to be happy with us (except for a few Santa Fe widows who had had their eyes on Cap).

The finest wedding present anyone ever received was a letter which came to us on June fifth. It was from Bernie Polk in Washington, D. C. Bernie was a lifelong friend of Dorothy's and had visited her and Cap the previous summer. Her letter stated in part:

"How happy I am over your wonderful news! When I was in Santa Fe Dorothy and I had many long talks. She told me that she knew she didn't have long to live and that her dearest wish was that Cap and Molly would marry!"

I was overcome on reading this. Cap was very quiet and

199

then said, "I never knew Dorothy had told Bernie that and it is wonderfully generous of her to write it to us. However, Dorothy had told me the same thing a number of times —that she wanted us to marry after she was gone. Somehow, I couldn't say that to you, not knowing if you'd believe it. Now Bernie has said it for me—you see how blessed we are!"

* * * * *

John, Cap's son, had married a fine girl just a few months earlier and Cap had gone to their wedding shortly after Dorothy's death on his way to a Pacific cruise that Dr. McGoey had recommended. Now Cap and I drove down to Las Cruces to see the other bride and groom who were living in the house Cap had given them. I, of course, had never met them, or for that matter had not met Bill and Kay, who were by that time in Alaska where Bill had a surgeon's contract in Juneau.

Phyllis had meanwhile come to Santa Fe to see mother and to be nearby when we were away. She stayed in our Casita Gallina. On our return from "our wedding trip" to see Polly and John, we hadn't been in the house more than an hour when the phone rang. It was Kay, in Alaska.

"C. O., Bill is terribly ill with a dreadful anemia. They have just flown him down to Seattle. I'm driving the car down with all our things as soon as I can get there."

I repacked a bag for Cap, and Phyllis and I drove him to a plane in Albuquerque and he flew out within hours of Kay's call. It wasn't exactly a peaceful and undisturbed "honeymoon"!

When Cap reached Bill's bedside he was quite sure that his son would not live long. He was white as a sheet and had only about twenty-five percent of normal red blood cells. It was a mysterious anemia whose cause never was definitely diagnosed. However, massive blood transfusions as well as a complete exploratory abdominal operation (which discovered nothing) brought him around. Cap returned home after Kay arrived in Seattle and he had extracted a promise from her that she and Bill would come to us in Santa Fe as soon as he was able to travel.

Phyllis returned to England and our casita was rented for the first time to Nan and Eastburn Smith who had leased

200

their larger home for the summer. Cap and I went happily to work on the place, which needed much attention after my neglect of it while I was at the Health Department and trying to take care of mother at home the preceding year.

By July Bill was able to travel and he and Kay drove to us for his recuperation. They occupied mother's room and bath. Kay helped with all housework and we all became fast friends and practically a "family." It was almost three months before the young Wards were able to start out for the East and to look for a suitable place for Bill to start his own practice of surgery.

Before they were to leave they insisted that Cap and I go on a belated honeymoon. They supervised mother's care —Kay read aloud for hours to her—and looked after the dogs and place while we went east to visit numerous friends and family from Chicago to Wisconsin, then on to Maine where Cap saw my wonderful camp and met Dottie and Halsey Gulick who were still running Sebago-Wohelo. From there we went to Westchester, New York where we saw Louise and family and saw Mary Dallas and her mother, Aunt Hat, who died two weeks later. Mary married a widower, Jim Hetherington, a few months later.

By the spring of 1961 mother reached something of a plateau, healthwise, and she was moved to a fine small nursing home on Canyon Road where I was on the Board of Trustees. There her excellent nurses could wheel her out-of-doors, it was less expensive and more homelike, and of course Cap and I went to see her daily.

One of many episodes shows her character and wit even in her greatly incapacited state. Shortly after she arrived at the House of St. Luke, the head nurse, Robin Brook, came into mother's room. Mother started to ask her a question and then lost her thread of thought. Robin said,

"I'm sorry, Mrs. Radford, I guess I'll have to get to know you a bit better before I can read your thoughts."

Mother grinned and said, "How could you be expected to do that when I can't read them myself?!"

Phyllis came over again in March. Diana, who had lost her first baby girl, in December had had twins, a boy and a girl. Phyllis spent some time with them before coming to us. She had already taken up mother's transatlantic "commuting" to keep the family together. She and mother had many pleasant chats, and Phyllis brought her vivid accounts of Liz and Peter's little boy, Rollo, in Germany and of the new twins in Minneapolis. Although Mary Radford never saw her greatgrand-children and she had no vision left to be able to see the photographs of them, her mind's eye took it all in and she often discussed these youngsters as if she knew them well. Phyllis's frequent good letters kept us well informed of their progress.

In August 1961 mother developed pneumonia. She'd had numerous bouts with such lung congestions before and with medication seemed to improve. When Bergere came to see her on the morning of August 19, the anniversary of my brother John's death, he found her in remarkably good shape. I had spent the previous night at the nursing home and had gone home to bathe and change clothes. When the nurse had come in to ask mother if she felt like having breakfast, she answered,

"Of course, thank you. May I have my usual bacon, eggs, and coffee, please?"

Two hours later she went into a coma with a smile on her lips. I held her hand as her pulse raced faster and faster and then the remarkable old heart gave up. She was almost eighty-seven. There was no grieving for her. I knew she was happy to be with her loved ones "on the other side."

1962-66

In the early winter of 1961-62 Cap suggested a trip now that we had no responsibilities except Dorothy and Cap's little Pit Bull terrier, Jenny, a sable collie named Susie, and a gorgeous Great Dane, Sandy, who had been given to us shortly after we were married. Cap and Dorothy had taken a few M.S.T.S. trips which were made on military transports carrying troops and material to our many overseas bases. Any regularly retired service man could get a ride on one of these if there was "space available." One made application for such a trip, got his shots for foreign countries, had a valid passport, and went to the appointed pier complete with baggage. If there was still space available when the ship was about to sail, the retired applicant and spouse (if any) could get on board and have a free ride except for paying the cost of meals. This never cost the taxpayer anything as the ship was going anyway. If active military personnel needed the space at any port, the "freeloaders" were promptly bounced off, no matter where the ship might be. Therefore, one had to be prepared to buy or hitchhike one's way back home.

I thought it a great idea and we sent in our applications for the M.S.T.S. Mitchel going to the Far East. (M.S.T.S. stands for Military Surface Transport Service.) Then we started to search for a "house-dog-sitter." One of our friends in real estate soon brought out a nice young man, Rick Gonzales. He was a teacher at the New Mexico School for the Deaf in Santa Fe. His roommate was getting married and he needed to move out and find a place in which to live temporarily.

Rick looked over the place briefly, learned what his few duties would be, and we settled on a token rent for utilities, etc. We were planning to be gone about six weeks but told him he could stay on in the Casita until he found another place or as long as he wanted. That was fine with him. When I asked him when he wanted to move in, saying,

"We've had guests recently but it will only take a day or two for us to get the place cleaned up," he glanced around and said,

"Can I go and get my things now? I'll clean up the place."

He moved in that January afternoon for two months and stayed over six years!

* * * * *

At Fort Mason in San Francisco we boarded the Mitchel and were led to one of the two VIP staterooms. What a trip that was! The passengers were a mixture of service men, their wives and children, of all sizes, shapes, and colors. All were in one class except for Active Service enlisted men who were unmarried who traveled in ordinary troop accommodations below. We visited with Cap's old Naval Academy pal, Vice Admiral Leon Fiske, and his wife who were living in Hawaii. We stopped at Guam and the Philippines and near the end of the voyage went to Yokosuka, the naval base in

Japan.

I had written Shinaye Osaki, my old friend from camp days whom I had last seen in 1928 when she and her family entertained us so beautifully. Now, over thirty years later, she met us at the Officers' Club and we had a day together. She enquired what we would like to do in that short time, and when she suggested that we might like to see the memorial to her wonderful father we enthusiastically set off together on the short train trip to Tokyo.

I have written in Chapter IV quite a good deal about Yukio Osaki and might add here that we had read that the militarists in Japan made several attempts on his life just before and during World War II as he was so strongly against them and their ideas. Post-war, during which his lovely wife died, he was called back at age ninety to head a provisional government! When he died, not too long afterwards, a private subscription was taken up by the Japanese people to build a memorial to this "Lincoln of Japan."

When we reached the memorial, we found it was built on a hill which had been the site of the hated militarist headquarters and overlooked the Imperial Palace. Unfortunately the museum was closed. However, it didn't take long for Shinaye to hunt up the custodian who opened the doors for us and we spent two or three hours with this great man's daughter showing us about. Some sixty-odd countries over the world had sent a great variety of gifts in Yukio's memory. Sweden sent a great slab of handsome marble properly inscribed. This stood at the entrance to the museum. From the United States there was a bust of Lincoln, and one of the South American countries, Bolivia, had donated a statue of Simon Bolivar—in each case drawing parallels between the great men of the respective countries. There were incredible jewels from India, beautiful rugs, and handwoven fabrics, books of other famous men, and many, many other objects too numerous to remember or mention. It was a most impressive experience. Unlike too many memorials, it cost and will cost the Japanese taxpayers nothing as enough individuals from all over the world had contributed funds to maintain it in perpetuity.

It was a perfect trip in all ways, and when we returned

after each of us had met new-old friends and relatives on the west coast, we were glad to settle down to our ranch life. Rick had taken wonderful care of the place and the dogs and we were more than happy to have him say he wanted to stay on with us indefinitely.

The following summer we received the sad news that Phyllis's husband, George Furness, had died suddenly at the early age of sixty-one. Shortly thereafter Diana had a third child, whom she named George for her father. Also, Liz had a baby girl in Germany. Both of these events gave Phyl a lift and we were glad that my sister had some of her family not too far away.

Cap and I decided on another trip—this a circuitous one—for the spring of 1963. We first took a small Norwegian freighter, the Granville, from California through the Panama Canal. Again we had good visits with his two sisters who lived in Whittier. He was once more very close to them after the long years of separation. We also saw numerous old navy friends of his who were then living in the San Diego area.

Both of us loving the sea, this jaunt on a very small ship was great fun. Cap had applied for "space available" on the M.S.T.S. Upshur, hoping that we could get aboard her in Christobal and stay with her until we got to Germany. It didn't work out quite that way!

After a beautiful trip through the Canal, we left the Granville and stayed overnight in a palatial looking hotel which was very much run-down since the Panamanians had taken it over shortly after Cap and Dorothy had been there a few years before. We started for the M.S.T.S. office full of confidence. Cap had never missed getting on board a ship, military or otherwise, in his extended travels—even when he bicycled for three years around a good deal of the world in the late forties. He had said more than once that someone always got sick, broke a leg, or got drunk at the last minute, and we would take the empty cabin.

We hadn't counted on Mr. Fidel Castro! All ships carrying military personnel in the Caribbean area were filled with men on active duty and/or their families, chiefly shuttling from Guantanamo and back again. Although the Upshur was to sail in one or two days, we were assured that there was *no hope* of our getting on her as there was an extra-long waiting list ahead of us.

We tried other commercial shipping offices but there were no ships heading for New York, let alone Europe, for many days to come and we had little desire to remain in the tropical heat longer than necessary. We found that there was a plane from Panama City, across the isthmus, which was flying to New York the next day and we booked seats on it. We asked about the one transisthmus train a day but it had left. So we hired a car and driver to take us the fifty miles to Panama City and drove off with the cab full of hot- and cold-climate paraphernalia.

Everything was fine until about halfway across, when the driver stopped practically in the middle of the jungle. He ruefully examined his tires and came to the window to announce that he didn't have *a* flat tire, he had *two* flat tires and only one spare!!

While Cap helped him remove our six suitcases, two coats, etc., from his car I stood at the edge of the road with my thumb pointed south (or really southeast as the Pacific end of the Canal is, surprisingly, east of the Atlantic end). I had done no hitchhiking since my college days and I didn't feel like the casual Hippie of today—not in such a place at such a time!

The traffic on that highway is far from heavy, or at least that was so that day. Two cars zipped by without apparently seeing "the damsel in distress." Then a small panel truck came toward us. By that time all our luggage was by the side of the road and the driver had removed his two ailing tires. The little truck stopped; the driver grinned at us and offered help. He was a small middle-aged man of indeterminate color and race—but his smile looked like heaven to us. He was an electrician and fortunately he was returning from a job in Christobal and the truck bed was almost empty of equipment and material.

I got into the small seat next to the driver, and Cap, our taxi driver, six suitcases, two coats, and two tires squeezed into the back. Our rescuer, Otto Claghorn, was not only hospitable and chatty but was extremely intelligent. Furthermore, he *loved* the United States and North Americans! During the thirty- or forty-minute drive he gave us a liberal education on Central America. He knew a great deal about Panama's economics, its agriculture, its politics, and even a good deal about its history. We listened to him with awe, at least I think Cap and I did. Our carless driver was probably too busy thinking about his problems before we dropped him and his tires off at a service station, one of the few along the route.

Reaching the environs of Panama City, our new friend who was part Honduran, part Indian, and some other parts, turned to us apologetically. He asked if we would honor him by stopping at his home and meeting his family before we got into the city proper. We of course were charmed and had a cold drink of tropical fruit juice and a visit with his family. His children ran out into the garden and cut us sticks of sugar cane, coconuts, etc.

We then started off for what we supposed would be our hotel in the center of town where we had made reservations by phone. Otto gradually let us know that he wasn't taking a direct route, adding,

"I know you Americans. If I take you right to your hotel you'll go to your room, take off your shoes, and won't see anything of my wonderful city!"

He assumed that neither of us had ever been there before, and we hadn't the heart to disabuse him of that idea. Both of us had seen a lot of it in former years. We did protest that we didn't want to take more of his time. To this he said that he had done his job for the day, adding, "Please, it would give me such pleasure to show it to you!"

And show it he did! For over two hours we drove past beautiful residences—out to Old Panama, stopped to see many churches, ruins, modern buildings as well as the Palace. In the latter place he knew one of the elaborately dressed guards and we were allowed inside where ordinary tourists weren't allowed. Then he said,

"I don't want you to go home without seeing the bad side of my city; that wouldn't be honest."

Thereupon, after rolling up the car window and carefully handing my purse back to Cap, he said, "I'm afraid everyone isn't honest; some of these very poor people might grab your pocketbook if they could reach it."

So we entered the stifling, fishy smelling slums, brushing against hordes of people of all sizes, races, shapes, and colors.

"Now, I will take you to your hotel, and when you get home you can tell your friends that you have really seen my city, the best and the worst of it!"

When the little truck drove up to our quite grand hotel, the doorman rather sniffed as two tired, dirty people with a pile of luggage extricated themselves through all doors of the vehicle. We shook hands with Otto, and Cap tried to pay him or at least give him a large tip. The little man wouldn't take a cent. He drew himself up with great dignity and said,

"You have given me great pleasure—it has been a happy day and I wish you a fine and safe trip home."

All we could say was, "Thank you, thank you."

As we flew over the lovely Caribbean we thought our adventures would simmer down a bit because, having family to stay with in New York, we were hopeful that sooner or later we could get on a transatlantic M.S.T.S. Unfortunately our plane from Chile was very late, necessitating an unexpected stopover in Miami to wait for a different flight. As we flew overland, close to Philadelphia, thick clouds gathered. We flew on in bright sunshine but could see nothing below. It dawned on us very soon that we were circling as the sunshine came in on one side of the plane, then on the other. This went on for almost three hours and all of us felt more than uneasy. The pilot finally announced that Philadelphia was "socked in" (as if we didn't all know it!) and that we were continuing to New York. The Philadelphia passengers were unhappy but those of us headed for New York were relieved.

The relief didn't last long as we again began to circle. After another hour or so the pilot announced that New York was "socked in"—no news to us—and we were returning to Philadelphia where we eventually landed in the dark and rain. The airline did put us up for the night and gave us transportation fare to New York the next day. Guess what transport we chose? The good old train!

"An ill wind—etc." That evening I phoned Tince Coffin, and old camp friend whom I hadn't seen for years. She and her husband, Roy, drove in from Marion and spent the evening with us. Again a fine reunion and a chance for Cap and my old friends to meet one another.

Our New York stay with the Dallas relatives was pleasant and rewarding. Cap was promised "space available" on an M.S.T.S. bound for Bremerhaven. Lunching the day before the ship was to sail, with another old camp friend, Helen Cowles Whittaker, we were mulling over the best way to get over to Fort Hamilton on the Brooklyn side with all our baggage. We had wisely shipped two of our big bags home. Helen seemed preoccupied and went to her desk, saying not a word.

Suddenly she lifted her head and said, "You know, the new Aquarium has just recently opened near Coney Island. I'd like to see it—if I can get hold of my chauffeur we'll drive you over." Happily we accepted.

As we approached the aquarium we found that the gates were closed and the sign said "Not open on Tuesdays." Nothing like that would stop our Helen. She sent Mike, the driver, in to see what he could do. The man soon returned grinning, saying,

"It's O.K. You can go in."

We all asked at once, "How did you do it?"

"Oh, I just told the man my boss was the President of the New York Botanical Gardens and had a visiting general who couldn't wait to see his show!"

When we were ushered into the place we found Mike's "man" was none other than the curator of the aquarium himself! (Should remember his name but can't.) This gentleman gave us a conducted tour of the entire place, introducing us to every specimen of flora and fauna as personal friends.

Don't we know the right people at the right time?!

As Helen and driver dropped us off at the BOQ at Fort Hamilton I heard the chauffeur say,

"You know, boss, Mr. Whittaker's plane is due at La Guardia in twenty minutes—we'd better step on it!"

The next morning Fort Hamilton men bussed us over to

the ship's side. We sat down in the terminal building to await our call to be assigned a cabin and go aboard. We waited and waited and waited. The ship gave the hour's warning blast for visitors to go ashore. When the half hour's blast came we began to feel like a bride left waiting at the altar. About fifteen minutes before sailing time our names were called and we and bags were taken aboard.

Cap turned to me and said, "See, I told you I never miss!"

"Well," I retorted, "what about the Upshur at Panama?"

"Even the United States government can't handle Castro!"

* * * * *

Liz met us in Bremerhaven, another first meeting for my loved ones. She drove us to Bergen-Belsen where Peter was then stationed. Peter, by then being a colonel in the British Army, had drawn quite a large house for their quarters. Liz pointed to a larger house next door and said,

"We were offered that one; it's very attractive but when I heard it had been occupied by 'The Beast of Belsen' during the concentration camp days I said, 'Nothing doing, I won't set foot in it.'"

We met four-year-old Rollo and six-month-old Kate, the Crookshank children, and had a happy four or five days' visit. The army and navy hit it off beautifully. We went to numerous officers' parties and soon all the attractive young men under Peter were calling my darling, "Uncle Cap."

We took a night boat from Den Heuck to Folkstone and soon were ensconced in the Old Bell at Malmesbury. Diana and two-year-old twins were visiting Phyllis, so there was another first meeting and reunion. By then all of my immediate family had met Cap and I had met his, in less than three years of marriage. Not bad for two "old newlyweds"—what was amazing was that we all liked one another.

Getting home was another tight squeeze. This turned out to be slightly different. Before we took the military bus from London to Southampton we were warned that there was "Space available" if we'd accept what "space" they had for us. Knowing that "beggars can't be choosers," and being Scotch enough not to refuse a free ride, especially after that unexpected plane ride to New York, we said O. K.

There was no waiting at the dock this time. As we boarded the M.S.T.S. Bruckner I was led to a tiny upper-deck cabin which I found I was sharing with an attractive army nurse and her delightful nine-month-old baby boy. With the crib in the room we had the choice of leaving the door to the companionway open or the door to the tiny toilet-shower room open. Also, Barbara and I had to take turns dressing as there was only floor space for one person at a time.

Cap meanwhile was led way below decks and found himself quartered with five young bachelor officers fresh from being stationed in Germany. Each day when we met for meals or a game of Scrabble if we could find a secluded spot, he would tell me that he was acquiring a liberal education from his roommates such as he had never had even when he was a bluejacket in the coal bunkers!

It being spring, the Atlantic was really rough, which he didn't mind but too many other passengers and their children were actively seasick. In such crowded conditions this was not pleasant and it was really too cold on deck to sit out and we couldn't walk all our waking hours. We were grateful for the free ride but glad to reach port. As the ship passed beneath the partly built Verrazano bridge on a lowering day we looked at the famous skyline of New York and decided we'd had enough of crowds, so took a plane from La Guardia to Portland, Maine. We hadn't seen Bill and Kay since they had settled in Rockland on Penobscot Bay after leaving Santa Fe almost three years before.

Kay was happily practically rebuilding the old house they were buying and Bill was getting enough good surgical practice so that he was almost ready to complain that his work interfered with his sailing! Those two crazy kids had selected this small town to live in just because of that sport. With Bill's extensive twelve years of training and his specialty of pediatric surgery, they should have been in a large city. However, really living meant more to them than money, and we heartily agreed with that.

The following December I was called to Washington. The rooming house my aged father was living in was about to be torn down and he had to be moved somewhere. Phyllis was coming over to spend Christmas with Diana and family, so I asked her to meet me in Washington. By that time the money which he had inherited from his loving sister Elizabeth, had run out and father was living on welfare. That was the time I found out how "welfare" was run in these United States.

I visited nursing home after nursing home. Those for which the welfare department would pay were all "desegregated." The natural result was that every one of these home had none but black patients—no whites would enter them! Desegregation, my eye!

I appealed to the doctor who had occasionally seen father and he came up with the name of a modest home which took anyone who could pay $175 a month. I visited that home and found that they had a room. I plunked down two hundred dollars and said I'd be back with father that day. I reported to Phyllis who had arrived quite ill, so she was in bed at the home of friends.

Then I taxied to the rooming house, called an ambulance, and had father carried out, protesting volubly, of his basement room. He had apparently had a slight stroke and was not quite rational. However, halfway to the nursing home he opened one bright brown eye, grinned at me and said,

"Is this the way you treat your husbands?"

I replied, "You'd be surprised how many times I've ridden in an ambulance with Bill and with mother too!"

Next I went to the welfare office and asked how much they paid any nursing home for their clients. The answer was $100 a month. I said "O. K. I have father in such-and-such a home. You pay your hundred and I'll pay the rest." Then I walked out, went to Union Station, and bought a ticket home. Phyllis was better and agreed that since I'd accomplished our purpose she would stay over and settle the few belongings in his room.

Three months later I received a letter from the nursing home saying that they'd received nothing from the welfare department. There ensued a long correspondence between us; meanwhile I of course paid the nursing home in full—they were taking good care of father.

Welfare stated adamantly that if any part of their client's expenses were paid by an individual, they would pay nothing! It didn't matter what they had told me before. Then at one point they said that there was now an opening for a patient at D. C. Village, which there hadn't been previously when I had visited that quite remarkable "old people's home." The letter added that if my father went into D. C. Village, they, the welfare department, would pay for all his upkeep.

My next letter said, "How much do you pay for a patient at D. C. Village?"

Their reply was, $250 per month.

I got off one more letter to them, a nasty one!

"You refuse to pay $100 a month when I'd pay $75, but you happily pay out $250 a month of the taxpayers' money for the same patient for similar care if I pay nothing. Thank you!"

Fortunately for everyone concerned, father died at almost ninety-seven a couple of months later. He had mentioned some time earlier that he wished his body to be donated to a medical school, and Phyllis and I gave our consent to this. What a complete waste! An intelligent, extremely well read, attractive man who had done nothing with his life except raise some finely bred dogs. Had he been endowed with a million dollars he probably would have gone through it in no time, but he might have done something with his extensive knowledge of nature, botany, birds, even children—when they were small he loved them and scores of them loved him. He always lived on others; what he did with what money came into his hands no one ever knew. He never took a drink in his life, nor smoked (he was extremely intolerant of those who did), nor was there ever a whisper that he "took up" with other women.

At one point a few years before he died, when I was in Washington I found a delightful retirement home there which was privately endowed. I took him there and he was accepted. He seemed delighted with the place and promised to move into it. Six months later I wrote the home asking if there had been some hitch or reason why he couldn't be admitted. They said no, they had been waiting for him, holding a room for some time but that when they contacted him he just told them he had changed his mind.

When I confronted him with this the next time I saw him, he told me that they had turned him down! I replied that I knew this was a lie. His rejoinder was, "Oh, well, they really did because they said I couldn't work and earn any money if I moved in, so of course I couldn't go!"

I had nothing to say to that except, "When did you ever work or earn any money in the past fifty or sixty years?"

That brought back to me an occasion a number of years earlier. Great friends of his who visited me in New Mexico told me they were sure he didn't have enough to eat. I was horrified and wrote him asking if that were true, and saying that if it was, I would certainly send him a little money from time to time.

At least he was honest in his reply which was, "No, thank you, I have enough to live on, but would you please send me one hundred dollars so that I can get a patent on a wonderful invention I have? It will mean a million dollars to you and Phyllis in the future!"

A psychologist or a psychiatrist should write his story. To cap the climax, about a year after his death an Internal Revenue agent came to our house to question me about my income tax return. I had taken some deductions for the months I had paid for father's nursing home care. The agent asked me for proof that father had been in the home. I showed him the cancelled checks and told him that he could look up the records in Washington. Then he wanted to know what father had died of!—at almost ninety-seven? My reply was that I had never seen the death certificate but presumed it was pneumonia. I then gave him the name of the Washington hospital where father had died—saying he could look up the records.

After having spent some hours and a lot of the taxpayers' money (I wonder what his hourly pay was plus travel expenses), the man left, mumbling something about my deductions would never be allowed unless I answered his questions. I never heard from the IRS again about this matter!

* * * * *

In late 1963 in Washington I had picked up a "bug" and was quite ill. However, we started on another M.S.T.S. Pacific cruise, but by the time we reached Hawaii my intes-

214

tinal trouble returned with a vengence and we flew home.
Cap caught the "bug" from me and it was finally diagnosed
as amebic dysentery! You can bet we stayed close to home
for the next two years.

* * * * *

DOWNS AND UPS 1966-?

Our first years had been wonderful on the whole, and after
son Bill had recovered we thought about little except our
own happiness. In that spring of 1966 Bill and Kay and her
charming father, Ed Livingston, came out to visit us from
Maine; Kay's sister-in-law came from Canada; and Cap's
younger son, John, and his wife Polly, who had adopted a
Navajo Indian boy, all came from western New Mexico. It
was quite a reunion, in the middle of which my niece Diana
Carpenter asked if she could come. We sensed she was in
trouble and said of course. Barbara Stevenson took in Diana
and some of the tribe were put up at a nearby motel. In the
midst of our pleasure at having them all with us, we found
that Diana's marriage was on the rocks. Added to that was
the uneasy feeling that Kay and Bill's twenty-year-old marriage was not going smoothly.

The unhappiness of others close to us gave us much to
think about but our own "idyll" was only really somewhat
tempered by increasing arthritis in Cap's hips. However, he
continued to work hard at Los Piñones and at his doctor's
urging walked and even ran a couple of miles around our
fence line.

By autumn we decided on another sea trip. With the war
in Viet Nam we didn't even try for a M.S.T.S. cruise, but
booked passage on the Santa Mercedes a Grace Liner from
New York to Peru. About two weeks before we were to leave
for the East, our dear daughter-in-law Kay telephoned from
Maine that she was leaving Bill. We immediately invited
her to go to Peru with us. She promptly accepted and we
were fortunate enough to get a reservation for her on our
ship.

After good visits with my Dallas cousins Louise and Mary
and their families, we met Kay and her father at the pier in
Newark. It was a fascinating trip. Our friends the Rufus

215

Carters who were on an engineering job in Panama, entertained us while we were there. This time we didn't have to hitchhike across the Isthmus! I had seen little of Mary Jane since our jaunts together on well-baby clinics twenty-odd years before. The Carters meanwhile had been in Teheran, Karachi, and other far-flung places and Mary Jane had written wonderful letters about their lives abroad.

Having a young and beautiful girl with us added to the spice of our jaunt. Kay was besieged by young ship's officers as well as some passengers. This did "our child" a world of good. (She was forty years old but looked about twenty.) The high point of the trip was our flight to Cuzco and then to fabulous Machu Picchu. The eleven-thousand-foot altitude did not bother us, who live at seven thousand, so much as it did others. However, the flight over the Andes to get there was in a nonpressurized plane and we all had to "imbibe" oxygen through tubes passed to each passenger.

When we arrived home in November our boy in the Casita, Rick Gonzales, brought over a lovely deaf girl, Dolores Walters, who taught with him. They announced that they were getting married in December. Could they please continue to live in the Casita Gallina?

We, of course, said yes and that we'd like to give them some sort of reception on the wedding day, December 27. Rick said it would be wonderful if we would give lunch to the immediate family and close friends.

That Christmas was something! The Spanish-Catholic wedding was in the morning. The "immediate family and close friends" consisted of fifty people ranging in age from seventy years to two, who had luncheon here! Our Christmas decorations included white poinsettias for the dining table. Later the real reception for two hundred and fifty persons was held at the Elks' Club. It was quite a day, and we felt almost like second parents to the bride and groom.

In the spring Cap and I went to his fiftieth reunion at the Naval Academy to which many of Cap's numerous surviving classmates came from as far away as New Zealand. It was a wonderful "gathering of the clan," and I met most of Cap's old friends whom I hadn't known before. Unfortunately, Cap's hips were going from bad to worse. We had to cancel

216

other visits in the East, and right after the Annapolis affair was concluded we flew home, Cap requiring a wheelchair at the airports.

Kay came out to us after her divorce and spent the summer. She went to the College of Santa Fe, going back to school twenty years after college to study for a planned new career in marine biology. She helped about the house and the place in general as it became increasingly difficult for Cap to do much real work.

By autumn Bergere Kenney had gone from A to Z in the pharmacopia trying to find some relief for the worsening pain Cap was suffering in both hips but especially in the left one. He recommended an Albuquerque specialist in arthritis and we went to the Lovelace clinic there in December. We were swiftly referred to the orthopedic surgeon, Dr. George Dixon, who strongly recommended surgical cleaning out of the joint and a metal cap placed over the head of the femur.

Cap, who is a "do-it-now" person, got Dr. Dixon to name the first feasible date for the surgery, which was done on the fourth of January 1968. Having the fine Gonzaleses to take care of the place (they'd already had a baby girl), I lived in a motel across the street from Bataan Hospital for the seven weeks Cap spent looking at the ceiling following his drastic four-hour operation. This was no fun for either of us. Of course Cap was not allowed to remain immobile as physical therapy is just as important as the surgery itself. So twice every day he was given and taught exercises to help restore his muscle strength and begin to bring back normal movement. Most days I went with him to the physical therapy department so that I could learn each step in order to follow up on the exercises for months to come.

Meanwhile, knowing that swimming would be one of the best forms of therapy, I was determined to have a heating system for our own pool. This led to my ordering a circulating pump, a filter, and a heater. In order for Cap to be able to have year-around swimming, I bought an Aqua-Hut after I saw one in use. This consists of a huge bubble-like plastic roof to be erected over the pool in cold weather. It is held up by compressed-air blowers and held down by many ropes tied into the concrete deck around the pool.

All of this was a very complicated as well as expensive piece of business to buy and install. However, by the time Cap had been home a couple of months and was able to be taken up there by wheelchair, the "bubble" was up, the water was eighty degrees, and circulating. His first swim was a triumph! Getting him dressed and undressed from winter wear to "birthday suit" and back was a major procedure. However, once he got down into the water, its buoyancy made it possible for him to walk on the bottom near the shallow end with no crutches, walkers, or canes. This, plus his being able to swim gently and unaided, was a morale booster as well as daily improving his strength in every muscle of his body.

We were lucky to be able to get some good nurses' aides, and with other great help from neighbors and friends all went surprisingly well. He was still on crutches months later, chiefly because the right hip was deteriorating rapidly. Neither of us had the courage to have the other hip operated on, but in the fall of that same year George Dixon, who had by then become a great friend, cut some major nerves to relieve the pain, and that took only two weeks of hospitalization.

By the winter of 1968-9 Cap was able to get about with two canes and we took a lovely Caribbean cruise from Los Angeles, passing through the Panama Canal going and coming. We stopped at Acapulco, Mexico en route, and one of the few of Cap's Navy classmates whom he hadn't seen for years and whom I hadn't met, flew down from his home in Mexico City. He, Jim Conover, took us on a lovely day's drive over that beautiful city and environs, and the two old friends had a fine get-together.

During the following summer the right hip became increasingly painful and George Dixon sent us to Dr. Roderick Turner in Boston's Massachusetts General Hospital. There the top orthopedic surgeons in the country were doing "total replacements" of the hip joint, using a new, experimental glue or cement. After removing the entire upper end of the femur and all of the acetabulum (the socket of the joint), they replaced the hip with a "steel" artificial prosthesis.

218

Only certain physicians in the country were allowed by the F. D. A. to use this glue which had been used for some time in England.

Dr. Turner, wisely I think, advised Cap that as long as he was able to get around at all he should wait another year, if possible. In that time he felt sure the new procedure would be well tested and that probably Dr. Dixon would be allowed to use it right near our own home. Relieved not to have immediate surgery so far away, we went up to Maine for a few days with Bill and his new wife, before flying back to Santa Fe. While East Bill had given his father a pair of "walking crutches" which Dr. Turner had advised. These gave him better stability and maneuverability.

On returning home Cap once more took up his furniture repair hobby which he had worked at periodically during the previous years. My laundry and sewing room we had converted into his shop. The washing machine, dryer, and mangle were still there for use. Since, my eyes had been failing steadily (macular degeneration of the retina about which I'd known for years), I could do no more sewing.

This hobby allowed Cap to sit most of the time, it gave him something worthwhile to do, but it was painful for him to walk and for me to watch him bent over on the crutches. I used to say to myself, "Please God, he'll be able to walk some day with a cane, but he'll probably never be able to straighten up to his magnificent erect posture!"

Even so we took a delightful cruise around the Hawaiian Islands the following January. Home once again, we resumed our life at Los Piñones. In the interim Rick and Dolores had left the Casita, expecting another baby and looking to a bigger job in California. However, they did not leave us before finding another newly wedded pair. These were Roland Fletcher, a fine young Englishman, and his deaf bride Phyllis who had been teaching at our School for the Deaf. Roland came in on a new basis, agreeing to work on the place in return for his rent; and what a fine job he did, taking care of the pool and garden work, etc. They came in the spring of 1968, had a baby boy on Cap's birthday in January, and left for a better job in Albuquerque a year later.

Again, before they left, a new delightful pair of young

people took the Casita and the job of taking care of us, the pool, etc. How lucky we were and still are! Each new tenant became our friends and our children. Mickey and Ed Crocker tiled the bathroom in the Casita and made many other improvements.

I had a brainstorm and in the spring of 1970 we decided to remake mother's old apartment, which was then a dining room and guest room and bath, back into a separate apartment. This was done by our old friend Sabino Varela from Pecos who had done so much work for us at the pool. This time Cap took to the newspaper an ad for a tenant. We wanted one person or a couple who would be willing to work for part of their rent and/or give us a hand when the Casita tenants were away.

The young man at the newspaper read the ad, tore it up, and said, "My wife and I would like to see it first. Have you a yard? I have a couple of dogs and some chickens." When Cap told him we had some forty acres Art Greiser and his charming wife Eileen came out the same day and moved in the minute the work was finished.

When Ed and Mickey and a baby boy (our third "grandchild" in the Casita in three years) moved out in the autumn, Art and Eileen moved into the Casita and the grandson of an old friend took the north apartment for six months. Now we had a third of the house we did not have to take care of and two sets of tenants to help take care of us and the place!

In October 1970 Cap went into Bataan Hospital for the third time and had his total replacement of the right hip. In four weeks he was home, in six weeks he was walking with *one* cane, and the day before my opthalmologist told me never to drive again, Cap was driving quite easily!

Carol Adams, a charming teacher from New Hampshire, moved into the north apartment on February Second, my 66th birthday, the day Ken Reid moved out. Cap and I left for a forty-four-day cruise to the South Pacific, Australia, and New Zealand shortly after that. He never used a cane nor took an elevator on shipboard; and we were *dancing,* Cap once more straight as a ramrod, when we came into port in San Francisco!!

220

One day in May, Art Greiser, our fine caretaker in the Casita Gallina, phoned Cap. "Would you like to be a grandpa?"

"Sure," said Cap, "but what are you talking about?"

"I've had a job for the last few days with Warner Brothers, who are making a John Wayne movie out here south of town. They say they need grandpas, and I thought you'd make a good one."

The upshot was that Cap and I reported the next day to, we suppose, the casting director for the extras needed in the picture. Surprisingly enough, among numerous Santa Feans we were signed up. The nice wardrobe mistress, Neva, fitted us with clothes suitable to 1876 and we and others were bussed to the "lot."

We spent three fascinating days at a rather godforsaken spot, watching and participating in one scene of "The Cowboys." Though the location was hot and dusty and there were many long waits and reshots made, we were completely intrigued by the entire performance.

The smallest detail was not overlooked in making this film. Modern eyeglasses and wrist watches were removed, even from those of us in the distance. Tire tracks were raked over, after each trip a sprinkler passed to settle the dust. If a jet stream appeared in the blue, blue sky or the distant sound of a car was barely heard, the cameras were stopped immediately.

All the personnel from cowboys, roustabouts, to important screen stars were friendly, helpful, and delightfully courteous. Huge trucks of wardrobes, comfort stations, as well as fabulous trailers for feeding everyone at noon, were supplied. To top it all off, John Wayne and his stand-in were almost always there among the crowd even when they had no part to play. The former, who treated us all as good friends, was like a big, amiable farm boy. His leading lady, Sarah Cunningham, was equally gracious and took the trouble to tell us the plot or scenario, during the long waits.

We never heard any shouting, argument, or fussing. John Wayne and Sarah Cunningham took direction and went through repeated retakes without a grumble or suggestion of their own. All and sundry brought their kids up to have their pictures taken with the famous star and he happily posed with each—including Cap and me!

It took a year before the movie came to Santa Fe. Many people here and there over the country saw the picture and recognized Cap—he was in one close-up shot. I could only spot myself standing in a wagon in the distance, simply because I knew where I'd been.

We treasure the photo and will always remember the experience, and especially the perfect teamwork of those wonderfully amiable people.

Carol, Eileen, and Art are still with us, this summer of 1973. In the last two years I have become Cap's first assistant in the furniture repair work. We've done about a hundred and thirty pieces, including dining room tables and upholstered chairs for about forty different friends. Right now I must get down to the laundry-shop. We have about five unfinished pieces on hand.

As the late summer of 1973 approached, Cap and I have had the great pleasure of a visit from England of Liz (Beebi, my little girl of 1940) and her two children, Rollo and Kate. They stayed about a week and once again we feel "caught up" with them. Liz seems to be coming out of her great tragedy of losing her wonderful husband, Peter, in early 1972, and the fifteen-and eleven-year-olds seem to have taken happily to this different life. We had them meet a few childhood friends of Liz plus a number of young people about the ages of my great-niece and nephew. Their short visit ended with a party at the pool with farolitos all about, plus the floating fairy lights on the water. The evening was a lovely one, with a fire in the fireplace for those who swam, candles on the mantel and the food table, and a bright half-moon shining over all.

The old place really came alive once again and we feel happily reunited with some more of the close family who live five thousand miles away, in spite of fifty and sixty years' difference in ages.

Cap is 79 and I'm 68 but there is still much to do. Home, Health, and Hobby—who could ask for anything more?